D1064825

HOLLIS DANN SONG SERIES

SONGS FOR PRIMARY GRADES

HOLLIS DANN, Mus. D.
DIRECTOR DEPARTMENT OF MUSIC EDUCATION
NEW YORK UNIVERSITY

BOOK ONE

AMERICAN BOOK COMPANY · NEW YORK

CINCINNATI · CHICAGO · BOSTON · ATLANTA

FOREWORD

Good vocal music is the happy wedding of the spoken word and song. Obviously, then, a singing vocabulary is an essential prerequisite of the appreciative rendition of music, and this vocabulary is best acquired in childhood through the imitative singing of rote songs. The singing of many songs with varied tonal and rhythmic content and worth-while texts, gradually builds up a singing vocabulary and at the same time develops facility in the use of the tonal and rhythmic elements of music.

Singing should also develop harmonic feeling. A practical way to develop the harmonic sense in the child is through the hearing of accompaniments. Hence the accompaniments to a large proportion of the songs are printed in the book, readily available for school and home use. It is taken for granted that home singing will be encouraged and promoted as an invaluable aid to the musical progress of the child.

The 200 songs in this book, including 50 folk songs of 20 nationalities, furnish an ample song repertoire for the primary grades which, carried over from year to year, constitute an adequate basis for the study of music reading.

Group singing necessitates leadership. Whether in kindergarten or high school, a leader is required to teach and conduct the songs. Children everywhere love to sing and are capable of beautiful singing. The results obtained, however, during the school music hour are determined primarily by leadership. The tempo, tone quality, diction, phrasing, atmosphere, and emotional reaction to words and music are dependent upon the ability and efficiency of the teacher. The beauty and charm of the song may be destroyed by poor teaching and inefficient leading.

Under the present plan of music teaching in the public schools, the classroom teacher does at least nine tenths of the teaching and conducting. Hence the enormous importance of the classroom teacher in the singing of songs. The conscientious teacher will make every possible effort to qualify as a capable leader.

Hollis Dann

SONGS FOR PRIMARY GRADES

NIKOLINA

Celia Thaxter

Arthur Foote

1. Oh, tell me, little children, have you seen her—
2. Ni-ko-li-na! Swift she turns if an-y call her,
3. In her lit-tle gar-den many a flow'r is grow-ing—

The ti-ny maid from Nor-way, Ni-ko-li-na?
As she stands a-mong the pop-pies, hard-ly tall-er,
Red, gold, and pur-ple in the soft wind blow-ing;

Oh, her eyes are blue as corn-flow'rs 'mid the corn,
Break-ing off their scar-let cups for you,
But the child that stands a-mid the blos-soms gay

And her cheeks are ros-y red as skies of morn!
With spikes of slen-der lark-spur, burn-ing blue.
Is sweet-er, quaint-er, bright-er e'en than they.

JOHN–JOHN–JOHNNY

Katherine Davis   Arthur Edward Johnstone

Allegro ♩ = 138

good green peas." "Run a - way, run a - way, run a -
fresh white cheese." "Run a - way, run a - way, run a -
all come true!" "Hur - ry in, hur - ry in, hur - ry

way, John John - ny, For I don't want an - y - thing at all."
way, John John - ny, For I don't want an - y - thing at all."
in, John John - ny, For I want to buy . them . all."

THE THREE SAILORS

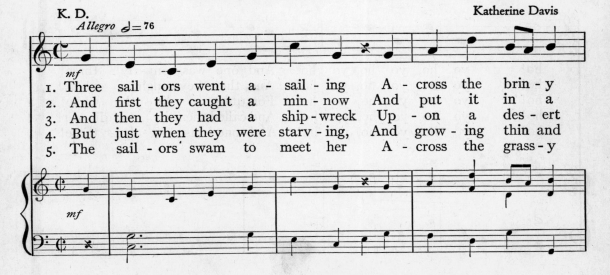

K. D.

Katherine Davis

Allegro ♩ = 76

1. Three sail - ors went a - sail - ing A - cross the brin - y
2. And first they caught a min - now And put it in a
3. And then they had a ship - wreck Up - on a des - ert
4. But just when they were starv - ing, And grow - ing thin and
5. The sail - ors' swam to meet her A - cross the grass - y

THE BAREFOOTED MAIDEN

Anthony Gillespie

Lydia Foote

AUTUMN COMES

Maxwell Gaddis

W. A. Mozart

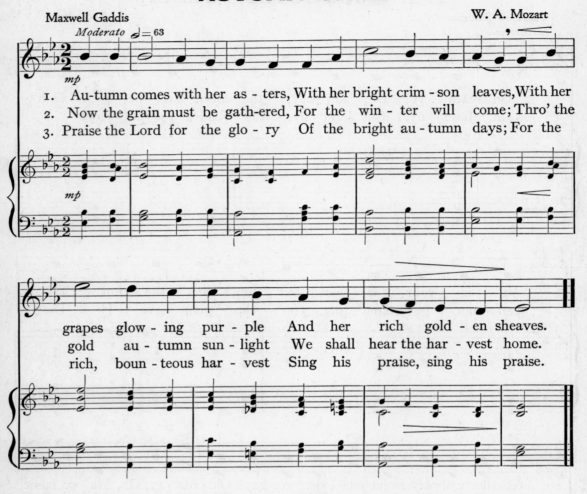

1. Au-tumn comes with her as - ters, With her bright crim - son leaves, With her
2. Now the grain must be gath-ered, For the win - ter will come; Thro' the
3. Praise the Lord for the glo - ry Of the bright au - tumn days; For the

grapes glow - ing pur - ple And her rich gold - en sheaves.
gold au - tumn sun - light We shall hear the har - vest home.
rich, boun - teous har - vest Sing his praise, sing his praise.

THE MAID AND THE PEDDLER

Ira Barton

Flemish Folk Song

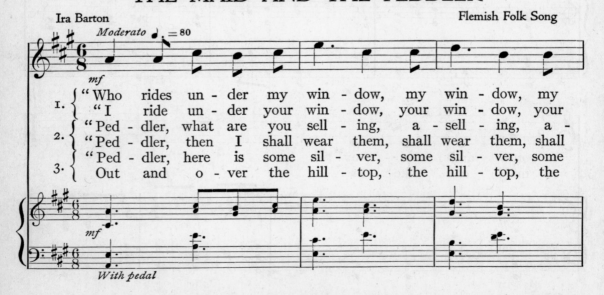

1. { "Who rides un - der my win - dow, my win - dow, my
   { "I ride un - der your win - dow, your win - dow, your
2. { "Ped - dler, what are you sell - ing, a - sell - ing, a -
   { "Ped - dler, then I shall wear them, shall wear them, shall
3. { "Ped - dler, here is some sil - ver, some sil - ver, some
   { Out and o - ver the hill - top, the hill - top, the

With pedal

UNDER A TREE

K. Davis

French Folk Song

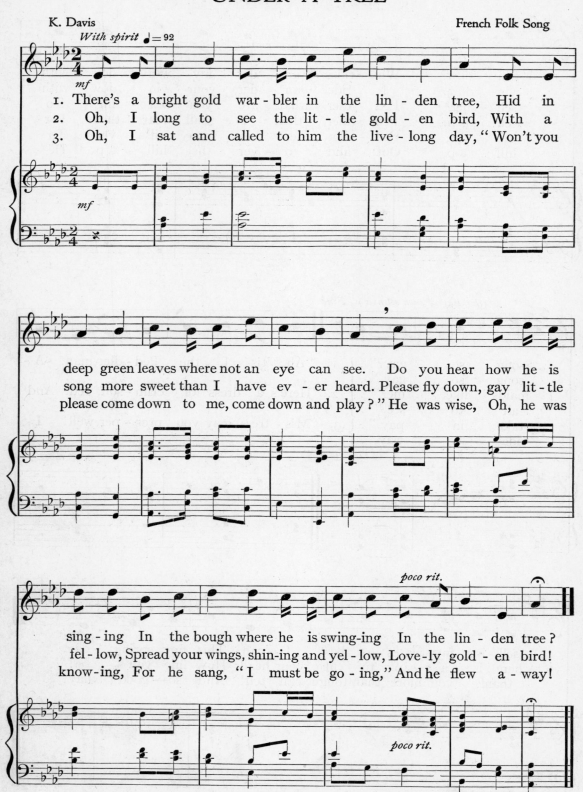

With spirit ♩ = 92

1. There's a bright gold war-bler in the lin-den tree, Hid in
2. Oh, I long to see the lit-tle gold-en bird, With a
3. Oh, I sat and called to him the live-long day, "Won't you

deep green leaves where not an eye can see. Do you hear how he is
song more sweet than I have ev-er heard. Please fly down, gay lit-tle
please come down to me, come down and play?" He was wise, Oh, he was

sing-ing In the bough where he is swing-ing In the lin-den tree?
fel-low, Spread your wings, shin-ing and yel-low, Love-ly gold-en bird!
know-ing, For he sang, "I must be go-ing," And he flew a-way!

THE SLEEPY GOOSE GIRL

K. D.

Hungarian Folk Song

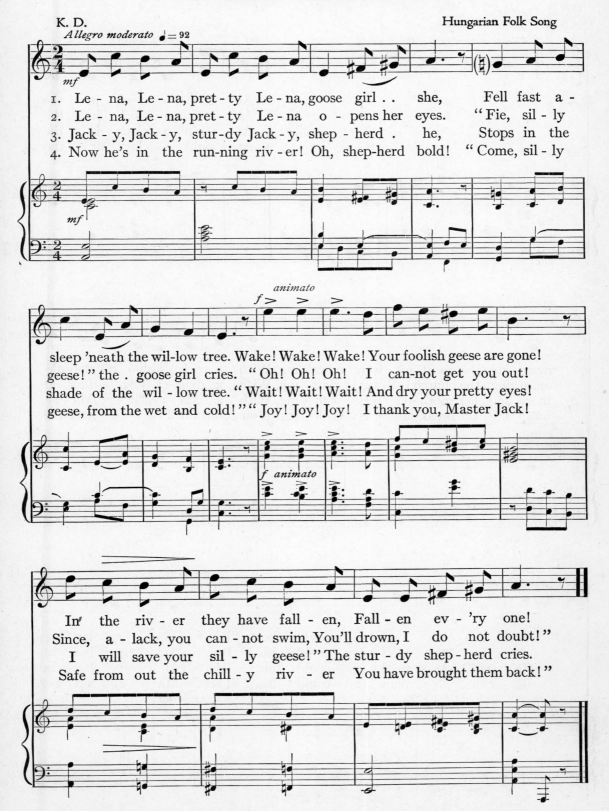

Allegro moderato ♩ = 92

1. Le - na, Le - na, pret - ty Le - na, goose girl .. she, Fell fast a -
2. Le - na, Le - na, pret - ty Le - na o - pens her eyes. "Fie, sil - ly
3. Jack - y, Jack - y, stur - dy Jack - y, shep - herd . he, Stops in the
4. Now he's in the run - ning riv - er! Oh, shep - herd bold! "Come, sil - ly

animato

sleep 'neath the wil - low tree. Wake! Wake! Wake! Your foolish geese are gone!
geese!" the . goose girl cries. "Oh! Oh! Oh! I can - not get you out!
shade of the wil - low tree. "Wait! Wait! Wait! And dry your pretty eyes!
geese, from the wet and cold!" "Joy! Joy! Joy! I thank you, Master Jack!

In' the riv - er they have fall - en, Fall - en ev - 'ry one!
Since, a - lack, you can - not swim, You'll drown, I do not doubt!"
I will save your sil - ly geese!" The stur - dy shep - herd cries.
Safe from out the chill - y riv - er You have brought them back!"

I WON'T GET UP

K. D.

1. At five o-'clock in the morn-ing the roost-ers were crow-ing, With a cock-a-doo-dle, doo-dle doo, . As loud as could be. But Ma-ry lay a-
2. At six o-'clock in the morn-ing the church bell was ring-ing, With a ding-a-ding-a-ding-a-dong, . As loud as could be. But Ma-ry lay a-
3. At sev'n o-'clock in the morn-ing her moth-er was call-ing, With a "Ma-ry, Ma-ry, Ma-ry, Ma-ry!" As loud as could be. But Ma-ry lay a-
4. At eight o-'clock in the morn-ing the break-fast was cook-ing, You could smell the cof-fee and the ba-con As plain as could be. Then Ma-ry left her

THE MAGIC VINE

Anonymous

Arthur Archer

Allegretto ♩. = 58

1. A fair - y seed I plant - ed, So dry and white and old; . . There
2. I watched it I tend-ed it, And tru - ly, by . and by, . . It

sprang a vine en - chant - ed . . With mag - ic flow-ers of gold. .
bore a Jack - o' - lan - tern And a great Thanks-giv - ing pie. .

Ped.

LADY MOON

Lord Houghton

Arthur Edward Johnstone

1. "La - dy Moon, La - dy Moon, where are you rov - ing?"
2. "Are you not tired .. with roll - ing, and nev - er
3. "Ask me not this, lit - tle child, if you love me;

"O - ver the sea, O - ver the sea." "La - dy Moon, La - dy Moon,
Rest - ing to sleep, Rest - ing to sleep? Why look so pale and so
You are too bold, You are too bold. I must o - bey the great

whom are you lov - ing?" "All that love me, All that love me."
sad as for - ev - er Wish-ing to weep, Wish-ing to weep?"
Fa - ther a - bove me, And do as I'm told, Do as I'm told."

A SONG OF THANKSGIVING

N. Grier Parke

Henry Fisher

1. 'Neath Au - tumn gar - land swing - ing, They pass in count - less
2. This Land we love so dear - ly, God bless her, still we

ranks; Their songs are glad - ly ring - ing With words of praise For
pray; Let ev - 'ry one sin - cere - ly, From coast to coast, A

fruit - ful days; With heart and voic - es sing - ing, The
might - y host, Re - count their bless - ings year - ly On

Na - tion gives her thanks, The Na - tion gives her thanks.
each Thanks - giv - ing Day, On each Thanks - giv - ing Day.

HDI—2

OCTOBER'S PARTY

The Home Book of Verse for Young Folks
Burton Egbert Stevenson

Arthur Archer

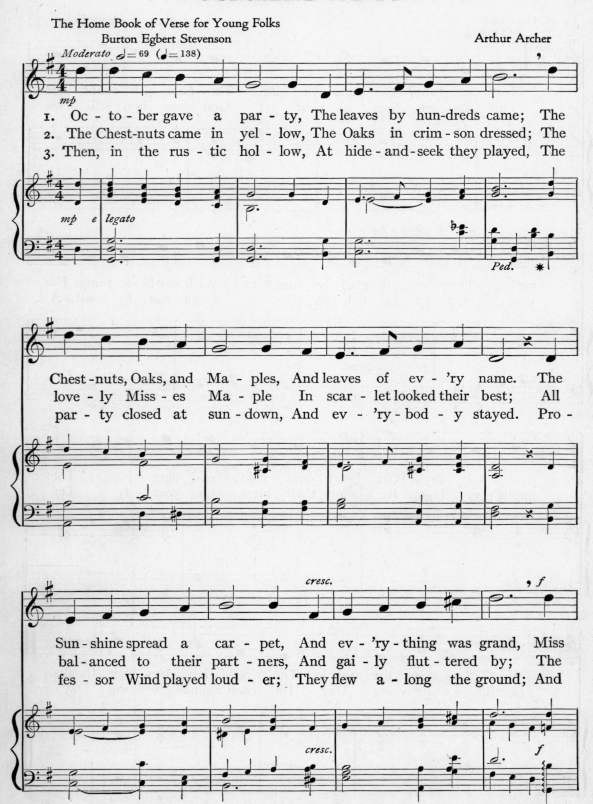

1. Oc - to - ber gave a par - ty, The leaves by hun - dreds came; The
2. The Chest - nuts came in yel - low, The Oaks in crim - son dressed; The
3. Then, in the rus - tic hol - low, At hide - and - seek they played, The

Chest - nuts, Oaks, and Ma - ples, And leaves of ev - 'ry name. The
love - ly Miss - es Ma - ple In scar - let looked their best; All
par - ty closed at sun - down, And ev - 'ry - bod - y stayed. Pro -

Sun - shine spread a car - pet, And ev - 'ry - thing was grand, Miss
bal - anced to their part - ners, And gai - ly flut - tered by; The
fes - sor Wind played loud - er; They flew a - long the ground; And

Weath - er led the danc - ing, Pro - fes - sor Wind, the band.
sight was like a rain - bow, New fall - en from the sky.
then the par - ty end - ed, In jol - ly "hands a - round."

TIMOTHY LEE

M. G.

Maxwell Gaddis

Allegro ♩. = 56 (♪ = 168)

mf

1. The hun - gri - est boy that I ev - er did see He
2. I'll go to the cook and the news I will break, Some

goes by the name of Tim - o - thy Lee, And this is the day he is
muf - fins and crumpets I'll ask her to bake, Some strawber - ry tarts and a

com - ing to tea. Heigh - ho! Tim - o - thy Lee!
choc - o - late cake. Heigh - ho! Choc - o - late cake!

THANKSGIVING HYMN

J. Lilian Vandevere

John E. West

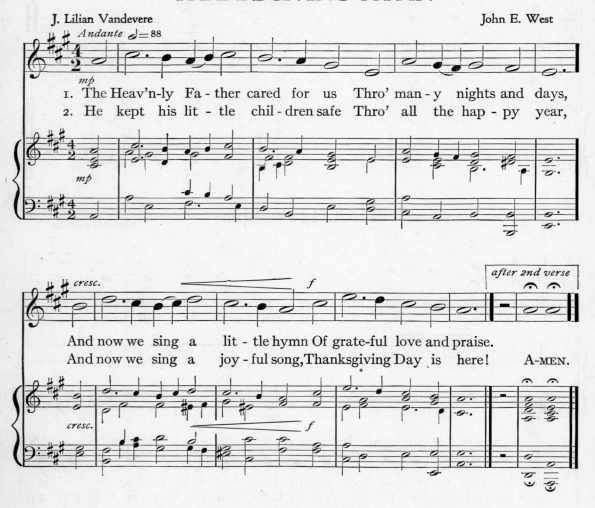

1. The Heav'n-ly Fa-ther cared for us Thro' man-y nights and days,
2. He kept his lit-tle chil-dren safe Thro' all the hap-py year,

And now we sing a lit-tle hymn Of grate-ful love and praise.
And now we sing a joy-ful song, Thanksgiving Day is here! A-MEN.

MY NATIVE LAND

N. Grier Parke

Arthur Edward Johnstone

1. My Na-tive Land, My Na-tive Land! Once fought for by that
2. My Na-tive Land, My Na-tive Land! For beau-ties rare on
3. My Na-tive Land, My Na-tive Land! Be-neath your ban-ner

CRADLE SONG

English version by Melissa Murphy

Swedish

1. Loo— loo— sweet lull - a - by, Loo— loo— sail - ing on high
2. Loo— loo— high in the trees, Loo— loo— lulled by the breeze
3. Loo— loo— sweet lull - a - by, Day - light fades from the sky,

To and fro while the breez - es blow My ba - by shall rock in her
She shall swing where the swal - lows wing, And float as she rocks in her
Work is o'er, and my arms once more My own lit - tle ba - by shall

cra - dle. Loo— loo— loo— loo.
cra - dle. Loo— loo— loo— loo.
cra - dle. (Omit . . . .) Loo— loo— loo.

SNOWFLAKES

J. Lilian Vandevere

John E. West

HUSH, MY DEAR
(CHRISTMAS)

Isaac Watts

Johann Sebastian Bach

Moderately slow ♩ = 66

mp

1. Hush, my dear, lie still and slum - ber, Ho - ly an - gels
2. Soft and eas - y is thy cra - dle, Coarse and hard thy
3. May'st thou live to know and fear him, Trust and love him

mf

guard thy bed! Ho - ly an - gels guard thy bed!
Sav - iour lay, Coarse and hard thy Sav - iour lay,
all thy days; Trust and love him all thy days;

Heav'n - ly bless - ings with - out num - ber Gen - tly fall - ing
When his birth - place was a sta - ble And his soft - est
Then go dwell for - ev - er near him, See his face, and

on   thy   head,   Gen - tly   fall - ing   on   thy   head.
bed   was   hay,   And   his   soft - est   bed   was   hay.
sing   his   praise, See   his   face, and   sing   his   praise.

GUARDIAN ANGELS

Robert Schumann

Simply ♩ = 54   *cresc.*

1. When chil - dren lay them down to sleep,   Two an - gels come, their
2. But when they wake at dawn of day,   The two bright an - gels

cresc.

watch to keep,   Cov - er them up, . safe - ly and warm,
go a - way;   Rest from their work of care . and love,

Ten - der - ly shield them from ev - 'ry harm.
For God . him - self keeps watch a - bove.

UNDER THE STARS

Adapted by K. D.

Margaret Coote Brown

1. Un-der the stars one ho-ly night, Je-sus, a babe, was born; . O-ver his head a star shone bright, Glow-ing un-til . the morn. .

2. Un-der the stars one ho-ly night, Je-sus came down to earth. An-gels in float-ing wings of light Chant-ed his glo-rious birth. .

3. Un-der the stars this ho-ly night, Christ-mas re-turns a-gain, Bear-ing its news of joy and love In-to the hearts of men! .

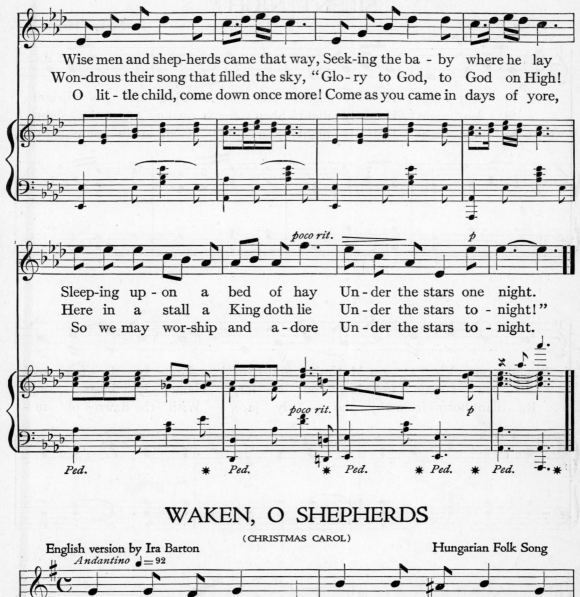

Wise men and shep-herds came that way, Seek-ing the ba - by where he lay
Won-drous their song that filled the sky, "Glo- ry to God, to God on High!
O lit - tle child, come down once more! Come as you came in days of yore,

poco rit. *p*

Sleep-ing up - on a bed of hay Un - der the stars one night.
Here in a stall a King doth lie Un - der the stars to - night!"
So we may wor-ship and a - dore Un - der the stars to - night.

poco rit. *p*

Ped. * Ped. * Ped. * Ped. * Ped. *

WAKEN, O SHEPHERDS
(CHRISTMAS CAROL)

English version by Ira Barton · Hungarian Folk Song

Andantino ♩ = 92

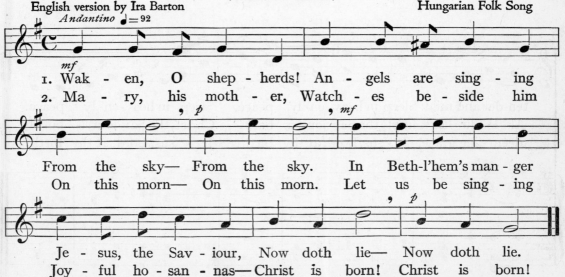

mf

1. Wak - en, O shep - herds! An - gels are sing - ing
2. Ma - ry, his moth - er, Watch - es be - side him

p *mf*

From the sky— From the sky. In Beth-l'hem's man - ger
On this morn— On this morn. Let us be sing - ing

p

Je - sus, the Sav - iour, Now doth lie— Now doth lie.
Joy - ful ho - san - nas— Christ is born! Christ is born!

SILENT NIGHT

Michael Haydn

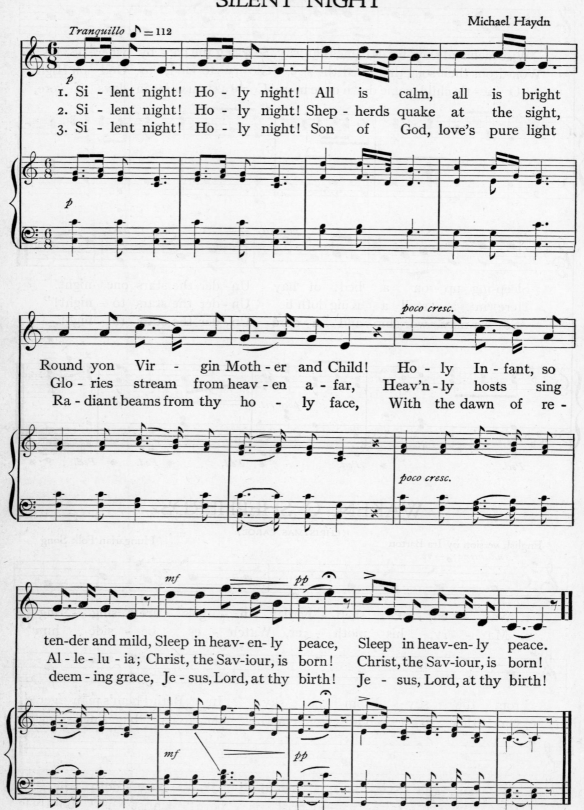

Tranquillo ♪ = 112

1. Si - lent night! Ho - ly night! All is calm, all is bright
2. Si - lent night! Ho - ly night! Shep - herds quake at the sight,
3. Si - lent night! Ho - ly night! Son of God, love's pure light

Round yon Vir - gin Moth - er and Child! Ho - ly In - fant, so
Glo - ries stream from heav - en a - far, Heav'n - ly hosts sing
Ra - diant beams from thy ho - ly face, With the dawn of re -

ten - der and mild, Sleep in heav - en - ly peace, Sleep in heav - en - ly peace.
Al - le - lu - ia; Christ, the Sav - iour, is born! Christ, the Sav - iour, is born!
deem - ing grace, Je - sus, Lord, at thy birth! Je - sus, Lord, at thy birth!

TWO CHRISTMAS EVE SONGS
I. BEDTIME

K. D.

Katherine Davis

Andante con moto ♩ = 72

1. Lit-tle chil-dren, lit-tle chil-dren, it is bed-time for all; Hang your
2. Lit-tle chil-dren, lit-tle chil-dren, be as still as a mouse! Not a

stock-ings at the fire-place By the chim-ney so tall. Hang your
whis-per, not a mur-mur, Not a sound in the house! Pull the

cresc - en - - do

stock-ings, big and lit-tle ones, Hang them neat-ly in a row, Then
cov-ers 'round your shoul-ders, Close your eye-lids, do not peep, So when

cresc - en - - do

scur-ry, scur-ry, scur-ry, scur-ry! Off to bed you go!
San-ta scram-bles down the chim-ney You'll be fast a-sleep!

NOTE: These two songs might be dramatized into a very small Christmas play. The first one is sung by one child who is the mother or the nurse, while a group of others, who are the children, act out the text. After they are all in bed the music might be hummed through once while they fall asleep. They are wakened at the beginning of the second song by the feet of the reindeer (six reindeer are enough), and they creep out of bed to surprise Santa filling the stockings.

II. SANTA CLAUS COMES!

Katherine Davis

1. I hear them, I hear them, I hear them on the roof! The rein-deer are com-ing, I hear each pranc-ing hoof! With a jin-gle, jin-gle bell and a clop, clop, . clop, And a-clat-ter, clat-ter, clat-ter, at the

2. I see him, I see him, I see him plain and clear! He's come down the chim-ney, Old San-ta Claus is here! In a love-ly crim-son cloak, with a sack full of things, Oh, he's fill-ing all the stock-ings with the

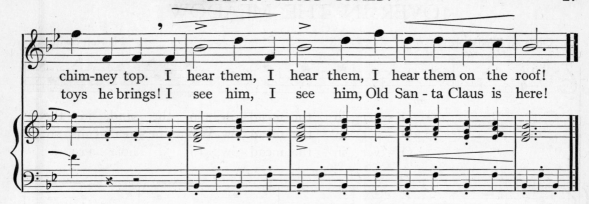

chim-ney top. I hear them, I hear them, I hear them on the roof!
toys he brings! I see him, I see him, Old San-ta Claus is here!

SLUMBER SONG

K. D.

Scotch Melody

Quietly and tenderly ♩= 84

1. Si - lent-ly, si - lent-ly, eve-ning is fall - ing, Drow-si-ly,
2. Ten-der-ly, ten-der-ly, moth-er will hold you, Long-ing-ly,

p e molto legato

Ped. ✻ Ped. ✻ Ped. ✻ Ped. ✻ Ped. ✻

drow - si - ly, crick-ets are call - ing; O - ver the mead-ow the
lov - ing - ly, she will en-fold you; Soft-er than shad-ows o'er

Ped. ✻

moon-light is stream-ing—Now should my ba-by be sleep-ing and dream-ing.
mead-ows a-creep-ing Down fall his eye-lids, and ba - by is sleep-ing.

OVER IN THE MEADOW

Olive A. Wadsworth

Newton Swift

Allegretto ♩ = 92

1. O - ver in the mead - ow, In the sand, in the
2. O - ver in the mead - ow, Where the stream runs so
3. O - ver in the mead - ow, In a hole in a

sun, Lived an old moth - er toad And her lit - tle toad - ie one.
blue, Lived an old moth - er fish And her lit - tle fish - es two.
tree, Lived an old moth - er bird And her lit - tle bird - ies three.

"Wink," said the moth - er. "I wink," said the one; So she
"Swim," said the moth - er. "We swim," said the two; So they
"Sing," said the moth - er. "We sing," said the three; So they

winked and she blinked In the sand, in the sun.
swam and they leaped Where the stream runs so blue.
sang and were glad In the hole in the tree.

EASTER

Youth's Companion   Newton Swift

Allegretto ♩ = 66

1. Give flow'rs to all the chil - dren This bless - ed East - er
2. Bright nod - ding daf - fo - dil - lies And pur - ple i - ris
3. And tell them, tell the chil - dren How in the dark, cold

Day, Fair cro - cus - es and snow-drops And tu - lips brave and gay;
tall, And sprays of sil - ver lil - ies, The love - li - est of all.
earth The flow - 'rs have been wait - ing Till spring should give them birth.

HDI—3

THE FIRST CHRISTMAS

Emilie Poulsson

Wm. Luton Wood

Andantino ♩. = 52

1. Once a lit-tle ba-by lay Cra-dled on the fra-grant hay,
2. By the shin-ing vi-sion taught, Shep-herds for the sweet Child sought,
3. And to-day the whole glad earth Prais-es God for that Child's birth,

Long a-go on Christ-mas, Long a-go on Christ-mas.

Stran-ger bed a babe ne'er found; Won-d'ring cat-tle stood a-round,
Guid-ed in a star-lit way, Wise men came, their gifts to pay,
For the Life, the Truth, the Way, Came to bless the earth that day,

Long a-go on Christ-mas, Long a-go on Christ-mas.

AMERICA

Samuel Francis Smith

Henry Carey

Moderato ♩ = 88

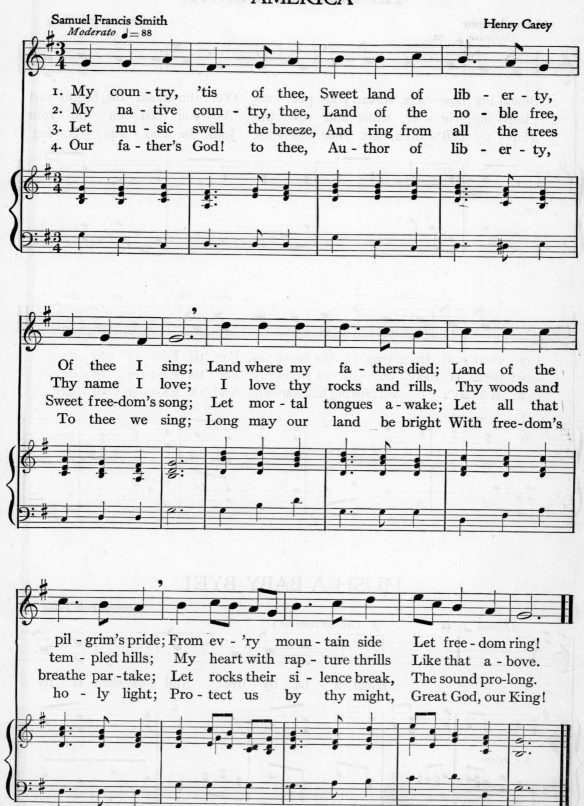

1. My coun-try, 'tis of thee, Sweet land of lib-er-ty,
2. My na-tive coun-try, thee, Land of the no-ble free,
3. Let mu-sic swell the breeze, And ring from all the trees
4. Our fa-ther's God! to thee, Au-thor of lib-er-ty,

Of thee I sing; Land where my fa-thers died; Land of the
Thy name I love; I love thy rocks and rills, Thy woods and
Sweet free-dom's song; Let mor-tal tongues a-wake; Let all that
To thee we sing; Long may our land be bright With free-dom's

pil-grim's pride; From ev-'ry moun-tain side Let free-dom ring!
tem-pled hills; My heart with rap-ture thrills Like that a-bove.
breathe par-take; Let rocks their si-lence break, The sound pro-long.
ho-ly light; Pro-tect us by thy might, Great God, our King!

'TIS EASTER TODAY

Melissa Murphy

German Folk Song

1. Bloom-ing flow - ers, spread your pet - als, O'er the mead - ow bright and
2. Sleep - ing riv - er, wake and rip - ple As you hast - en on your
3. Hap - py chil - dren, lift your voic - es, Join the cho - rus ris - ing

gay; Pour your fra-grance on the breez - es, For 'tis East - er to - day.
way; Birds of heav - en, car - ol sweet - ly, For 'tis East - er to - day.
gay; Win-ter's o - ver, Spring has found us And 'tis East - er to - day.

HUSH–A–BABY–BYE!

German Folk Song

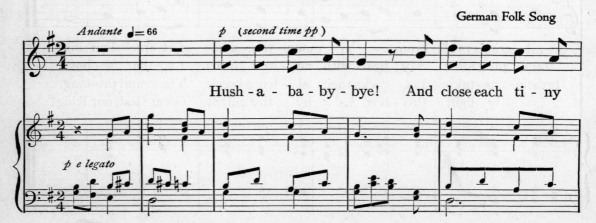

Hush - a - ba - by - bye! And close each ti - ny

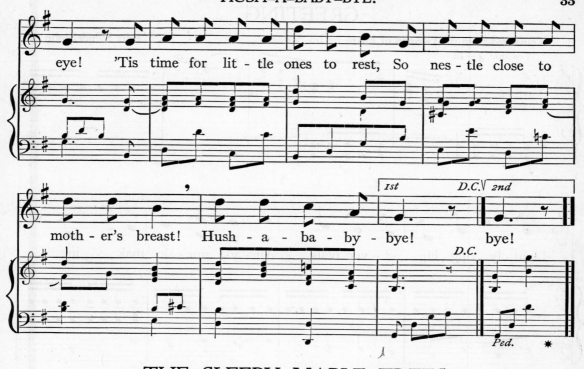

eye! 'Tis time for lit - tle ones to rest, So nes - tle close to

moth - er's breast! Hush - a - ba - by - bye! bye!

THE SLEEPY MAPLE TREES

Eleanor Hammond   Arthur Archer

Andante moderato ♩ = 66

1. I think they must be sor - ry— The lit - tle Ma - ple trees—That they
2. They nev - er see Thanks - giv - ing Nor Hal - low - een at all, Be -
3. Poor lit - tle tired . . Ma - ples, ⨯ Sleep - ing in the breeze, They

go to bed too ear - ly To see hol - i - days like these!
cause they go so fast a - sleep So ear - ly in the fall.
miss the great - est fun of all— They can't be Christ - mas trees!

GREETING

Translated from the German of Heine by Ira Barton

Felix Mendelssohn

Light - ly ring - ing sil - ver bells, Air - y mu - sic mak - ing,

Tell you tales of spring's re - turn, Earth and air a -

wak - - ing.

Where the gen-tle vio-let grows, Sound your music fleet-ing, Should you see a crim-son rose, Say, "I give you greet - - ing!"

HALLOWEEN

J. Lilian Vandevere

John E. West

Andante ♩ = 88

1. It must be Hal-low-een, For when I hur-ried by, A
2. He grinned with all his teeth From high up-on a shelf; I

Jack-o'-lan-tern stared at me And winked his yel-low eye.
did-n't feel a-fraid, be-cause I'd cut him out my-self.

AT TWELVE O'CLOCK

Katherine Davis

1. At twelve o'-clock the bells do ring— Ding dong!— Ding
2. Good-bye, good-bye, and rest you well, Old Year, Old

dong! At twelve o'-clock the peo-ple say A
Year! The bright new days be-fore us brim With

song— A song. The poor Old Year, so pale and thin, Slips
cheer, With cheer. Come sing we now, old friends and new, From

out a-mid the joy-ous din, And the lit-tle New Year, and the
hearts that all beat high and true, "O a Hap-py New Year, O a

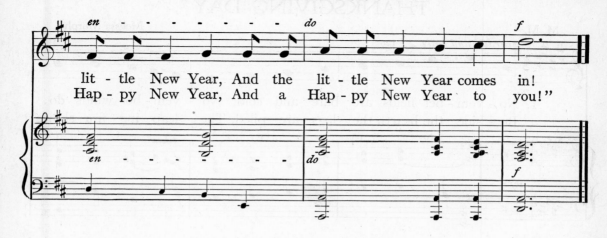

lit - tle New Year, And the lit - tle New Year comes in!
Hap - py New Year, And a Hap - py New Year to you!"

I SAW THREE SHIPS

English Traditional Melody

1. I saw three ships come sail-ing in
2. And what was in those ships all three? *On Christmas Day, On Christmas Day,*
3. Our Sav-iour Christ and his la - dy

I saw three ships come sail-ing in
And what was in those ships all three? *On Christmas Day in the morn - ing.*
Our Sav-iour Christ and his la - dy

4. Pray, whither sailed those ships all three?
5. Oh, they sailed into Bethlehem.
6. And all the bells on earth shall ring.
7. And all the angels in Heaven shall sing.

THANKSGIVING DAY

Melissa Murphy

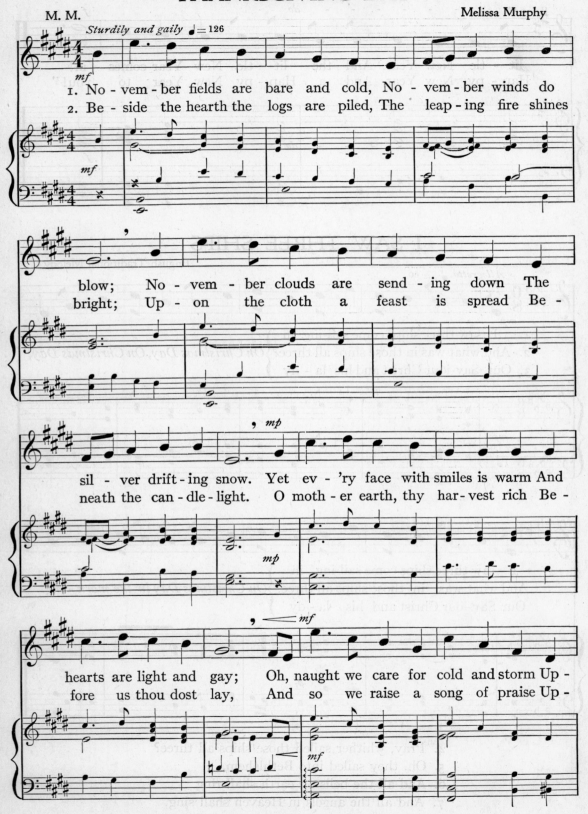

1. No - vem - ber fields are bare and cold, No - vem - ber winds do
2. Be - side the hearth the logs are piled, The leap - ing fire shines

blow; No - vem - ber clouds are send - ing down The
bright; Up - on the cloth a feast is spread Be -

sil - ver drift - ing snow. Yet ev - 'ry face with smiles is warm And
neath the can - dle - light. O moth - er earth, thy har - vest rich Be -

hearts are light and gay; Oh, naught we care for cold and storm Up -
fore us thou dost lay, And so we raise a song of praise Up -

on Thanks-giv - ing Day, . . Up - on Thanks-giv - ing Day!
on Thanks-giv - ing Day, . . Up - on Thanks-giv - ing Day!

NUTTING SONG

H. W. L.

Harvey Worthington Loomis

Con spirito ♩ = 132

1. Come, run a - long, run a - long, boys; Let's hur - ry to the grove of
   we! Bring a pail, bring a pail, boys; We're hunt-ing for the best of

wal - nuts, While we all sing a song, sing a song, boys; The
all nuts. Beat the trees with a rail, with a rail, boys; Let

1st

weath-er has a touch of frost. 2. But what care
(Omit . . . .)

2nd

not a sin-gle one be lost. . .

THANKSGIVING

J. Lilian Vandevere

Clarence Butler

1. Treas - ures from the gar - den, Fruit from or - chard trees,
2. Sun - ny days to play in, Star - ry nights to rest,

Hon - ey that was stored a - way By bus - y gold-en bees;
Home with all its hap - pi - ness And those we love the best;

Dates from the palm trees, Far in the East—
God's care to keep us All through the year, .

All of these have come to make A fine Thanksgiv-ing feast.
Man-y bless-ings help to fill Thanksgiv - ing Day with cheer.

THE STORY OF A PUMPKIN

Melissa Murphy

English Melody

1. A lit-tle pump-kin grew in the pump-kin field;
2. There came a lit-tle maid to the pump-kin field;
3. "Now see, my moth-er dear, what I've brought you here!"
4. The hol-i-day has come and the ta-ble's laid;

(Oh, but his cheeks, they are yel-low!) He . . rip-ened day by day, as the
(Oh, but her hair, it is yel-low!) She . saw the pump-kin gay and she
(Oh, what a feast's in the mak-ing!) We shall have a pump-kin pie in the
(Oh, what a day to be liv-ing!) Now we cast a hun-gry eye on the

min-utes sped a-way, In the sun-light so mel-low.
car-ried him a-way. (Oh, the fine, gloss-y fel-low!)
twin-kling of an eye, In the ov-en a-bak-ing!
yel-low pump-kin pie— So hur-rah for Thanks-giv-ing!

UP THE MOUNTAIN

Moravian Folk Song

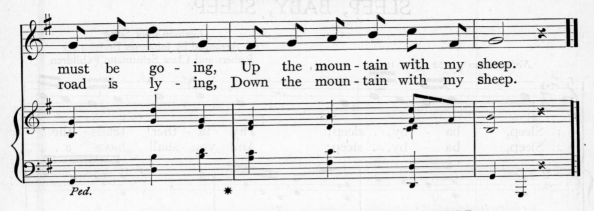

must be go - ing, Up the moun - tain with my sheep.
road is ly - ing, Down the moun - tain with my sheep.

Ped. *

UNDERNEATH THE WILLOWS

K. D.

Folk Song of Little Russia

Andante ♩=72 mp

1. Un - der-neath the wil - lows Where the brook is
2. Un - der-neath the wil - lows When the larks are

mp

p Allegretto ♩=84

flow - ing, Lit - tle rip - ples dash a - long And whirl with bright com -
nest - ing, Lit - tle birds a - wake from sleep And fill the day with

D.C.

mo - tion; Swift and gay they flow a - way To meet the might - y o - cean.
sing - ing; Light and fair, they mount the air To heav - en glad - ly wing - ing!

D.C.

SLEEP, BABY, SLEEP

German Folk Song
Arranged by Johannes Brahms for
Robert and Clara Schumann's children

1. Sleep, ba - by, sleep; Thy fa - ther tends the
2. Sleep, ba - by, sleep; And you shall have a

sheep; Thy moth - er shakes the dream - land tree And
sheep; And he shall have a gold - en bell And

down come all the dreams for thee. Sleep, ba - by,
play with ba - by in the dell. Sleep, ba - by,

sleep.
sleep.

(After 2nd verse)

GOING TO LONDON

Mary Mapes Dodge   Arthur Foote

1. Up, down! Up, down! All the way to Lon - don town—
2. Up, down! Up, down! All the way to Lon - don town—
3. Up, down! Up, down! All the way to Lon - don town—

Here we go with ba - by! I'm the pa - pa, You're the mam-ma,
See how fast we're go - ing! Feel the jar Of . . the car?
Here we are this min - ute! Rock a chair An - y - where,

You're the pret - ty la - dy! la - dy! la - dy!
Feel the wind a - blow - ing? blow - ing? blow - ing?
When we two are in it! in it! in it!

From *St. Nicholas Songs.* Used by permission of the publishers, D. Appleton-Century Co., Inc.

HDI—4

CRADLE HYMN

Martin Luther
(Written for his children)

J. E. Spilman

Andante grazioso ♩ = 104

1. A - way in a man - ger, No crib for his bed, The lit - tle Lord
2. Be near me, Lord Je - sus, I ask thee to stay Close by me for -

Je - sus Lay down his sweet head; The stars in the heav - ens Looked
ev - er And love me, I pray; Bless all the dear chil - dren In

down where he lay, The lit - tle Lord Je - sus A - sleep in the
thy ten - der care, And take us to heav - en To live with thee

hay. The cat - tle are low - ing, The poor ba - by wakes, But lit - tle Lord
there. A - way in a man - ger, No crib for his bed, The lit - tle Lord

più mosso

Je - sus No cry - ing he makes; I love thee, Lord Je - sus, Look
Je - sus Lay down his sweet head; The stars in the heav - ens Looked

down from the sky And stay by my cra - dle To watch lull - a - by.
down where he lay, The lit - tle Lord Je - sus, A - sleep in the hay.

SPRING MORNING

Clarence Butler

1. Leave your bed, sleep - y head, Rise and cease your yawn - ing!
2. Dais - ies bold, white and gold, Strew the grass - y mead - ow,
3. On the stream rip - ples gleam Where the sun is glanc - ing.

Come with me, wan - der free, While the day is . . dawn - ing.
Larks take wing, lin - nets sing From the wood - land shad - ow.
Com - rade, say! Come a - way! O'er the mead - ow danc - ing.

BIRD SONGS

K. D.

Katherine Davis

1. The rob-in sings in the ap-ple tree,
2. The cuck-oo sings when the day is fair,
3. The great owl sings at the end of day,

"Cheer up! cheer up!" mer-ri-ly. The rob-in sings in the
"Cuck-oo! cuck-oo!" ev-'ry-where. The cuck-oo sings when the
"Whoo Whoo!" far a-way. The great owl sings at the

ap-ple tree, "Cheer up! Cheer up!" mer-ri-ly!
day is fair, "Cuck-oo! Cuck-oo!" ev-'ry-where.
end of day, "Whoo Whoo!" far a-way.

PRAISE YE THE LORD!

Polish Melody

Praise ye the Lord! O come to-day with sing - ing! Bless ye the

Lord, All hon - or to him bring - ing! Come, all ye chil - dren,

His great love pro - claim; Kneel and a - dore him, Ho - ly is his name!

WITH HAPPY VOICES SINGING

F. M. Manzer

Moderato ♩ = 120

1. With hap - py voic - es sing - ing, Thy chil - dren, Lord, ap - pear; Their
2. For skies of gold - en splen - dor, For az - ure roll - ing sea, For

joy - ous prais - es bring - ing In an - thems full and clear.
blos - soms sweet and ten - der, O Lord, we wor - ship thee.

THE CHIMNEY SWEEP

K. D.

Katherine Davis

1. Sweep, sweep, chim-ney sweep, Ear-ly in the morn-ing I
2. Sweep, sweep, chim-ney sweep, Walk-ing on the roof with an

hear you call. Sweep, sweep, chim-ney sweep,
eas-y pace; Sweep, sweep, chim-ney sweep,

Climb-ing to the top of the hous-es tall. Does your moth-er know you have
Dropping down the flue to the chim-ney place. Up you come a-gain with your

climbed so high, Walk-ing all a-bout be-neath the sky? Sweep, sweep,
soot-y pack! Mer-cy good-ness me, but a sweep gets black! Sweep, sweep,

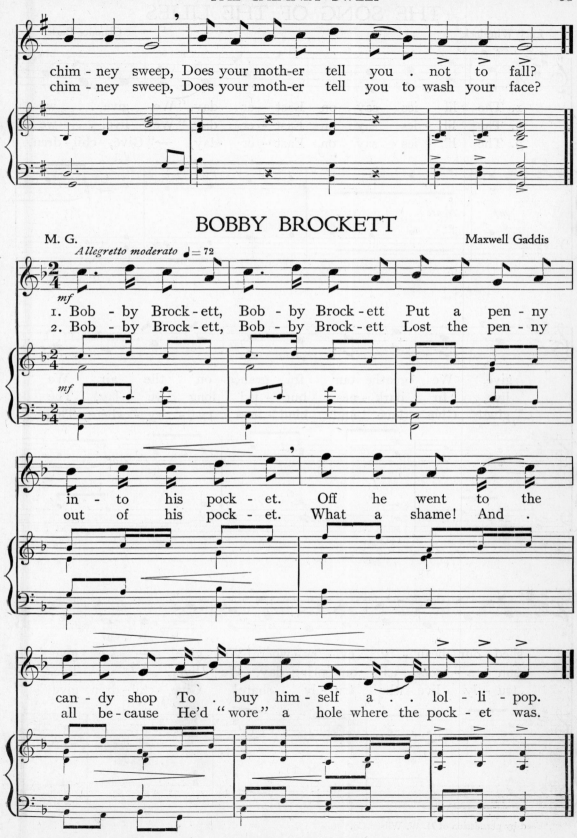

chim - ney sweep, Does your moth-er tell you . not to fall?
chim - ney sweep, Does your moth-er tell you to wash your face?

BOBBY BROCKETT

M. G.
Maxwell Gaddis

Allegretto moderato ♩ = 72

mf

1. Bob - by Brock-ett, Bob - by Brock-ett Put a pen - ny
2. Bob - by Brock-ett, Bob - by Brock-ett Lost the pen - ny

in - to his pock - et. Off he went to the
out of his pock - et. What a shame! And .

can - dy shop To . buy him-self a . lol - li - pop.
all be - cause He'd "wore" a hole where the pock - et was.

THE SONG OF THE LILIES

Lucy Wheelock*

Clarence Butler

1. The lil - ies say on East - er day, "We give, .. we give, We breathe our fra - grance on the air, We shed our beau - ty ev - 'ry - where! We give, — we give."

2. The lil - ies say on East - er day, "We live, .. we live, In dark - ness bur - ied long we lay, The sun a - woke us one spring day, We live, — we live."

3. The lil - ies say on East - er day, —"Give, chil - dren, give! Give love and kind - ness ev - 'ry - where; They tru - ly live who tru - ly share! Give, chil - dren, give!"

*Used by permission of H. W. Wilson Co.

THE SHEPHERDESS*

English version by Maxwell Gaddis

Old French Song

Moderately fast ♩ = 72

mp

1. Thro' the val-ley dark and deep, Shep-herd maid-en, drive your sheep;
2. In the val-ley dark and deep I have lost my sil-ly sheep!

mf

Has-ten past the crys-tal foun-tain, Do not rest up-on the
For I lin-gered by the foun-tain, And I rest-ed on the

rit.

moun-tain, For when night be-gins to fall, Hun-gry wolves will catch them all.
moun-tain, And when night be-gan to fall, I had lost them, one and all.

*This may be used as a game, played like the first part of London Bridge. The shepherdess goes behind the sheep and avoids being caught. On the word "all" a sheep is captured. Repeat this stanza until there are no sheep left. Then the shepherdess sings.

AUTUMN

K. D.

Robert Schumann

Allegretto ♩. = 112

1. The as-ters by the brook-side Are drows-ing in the sun, The
2. The pur-ple grapes are rip-'ning A-gainst the gar-den wall; O

sleep-y brook goes mur-m'ring And half for-gets to run.
la-zy, gold-en Au-tumn, I love you best of all!

CHRISTMAS DAY IN THE MORNING

Myles B. Foster

Now 'tis the mer-ry Christ-mas time, And the church-bells peal a joy-ous chime O'er fields of vir-gin snow; . . And to the church all decked with green, A-long each path-way may be seen The grate-ful peo-ple go! . .

SONG OF THE FIELDS

L. F.

Lydia Foote

1. A - plough-ing, a - plough-ing, a - plough-ing we will go. Now
2. A - plant-ing, a - plant-ing, a - plant-ing we will go. O
3. A - reap-ing, a - reap-ing, a - reap-ing we will go. We'll

spring has come with balm - y air, We'll make a fur - row
gold - en seeds that light - ly fall, Put forth your leaves so
bear the sheaves of rip - ened grain A - cross the mead - ow

long and fair! Sing ho - ho - ho! A - ploughing we will go!
green and tall! Sing ho - ho - ho! A - plant-ing we will go!
home a - gain! Sing ho - ho - ho! A - reap - ing we will go!

KINDNESS

Friedrich Silcher

Brightly ♩ = 76

1. Lit - tle drops of wa - ter, Lit - tle grains of sand,
2. Lit - tle deeds of kind - ness, Lit - tle words of love,
3. Lit - tle seeds of mer - cy Sown by youth - ful hands,

Make the might - y o - cean And the beau - teous land.
Make our earth an E - den Like the heav'ns a - bove.
Grow to bless the na - tions Far in oth - er lands.

THE AUTUMN WIND

J. L. V.

J. Lilian Vandevere

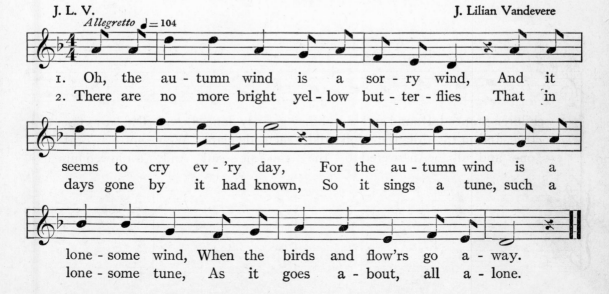

Allegretto ♩ = 104

1. Oh, the au - tumn wind is a sor - ry wind, And it
2. There are no more bright yel - low but - ter - flies That in

seems to cry ev - 'ry day, For the au - tumn wind is a
days gone by it had known, So it sings a tune, such a

lone - some wind, When the birds and flow'rs go a - way.
lone - some tune, As it goes a - bout, all a - lone.

THE PIPER

Lydia Foote

Netherlands Air

1. The pip - er walked the
2. The pip - er bowed and
3. But when the pip - er

vil - lage street, Loo - ra, loo - ra, lee! The folk ran out, the
passed his hat. Loo - ra, loo - ra, loo! But though he'd piped so
left the town, Loo - ra, loo - ra, lay! The vil - lage chil - dren

children pranced, Round and round they gai - ly danced, And Oh, 'twas fine to
true and fair, All the folk did then de-clare, "We've not a cent for
one and all An - swered to the mu - sic's call And fol - lowed him a -

see! Loo - ra, lee, Loo - ra, lee! Fine to see, fine to see! .
you! Loo - ra, loo, Loo - ra, loo! Not for you, not for you!"
way. Loo - ra, lay, Loo - ra, lay! Far a - way, far a - way!

SPRING IS HERE

Josephine Pease

German Folk Song

Moderately fast ♩ = 84

mf

1. Blos - soms sweet At our feet, Hear the spring-time call - ing!
2. Blos - soms fair, Dream - ing there, Long have you been sleep - ing.
3. Blos - soms dear, Spring is here, With her love - ly laugh - ter.

mf

poco rit.

Skies of blue Wait for you. Gen - tle rains are fall - ing.
Safe, I know, 'Neath the snow, In your moth - er's keep - ing.
And ere long, With a song, Sum - mer fol - lows aft - er!

poco rit.

INDIAN LULLABY

Charles Myall

Arthur Edward Johnstone

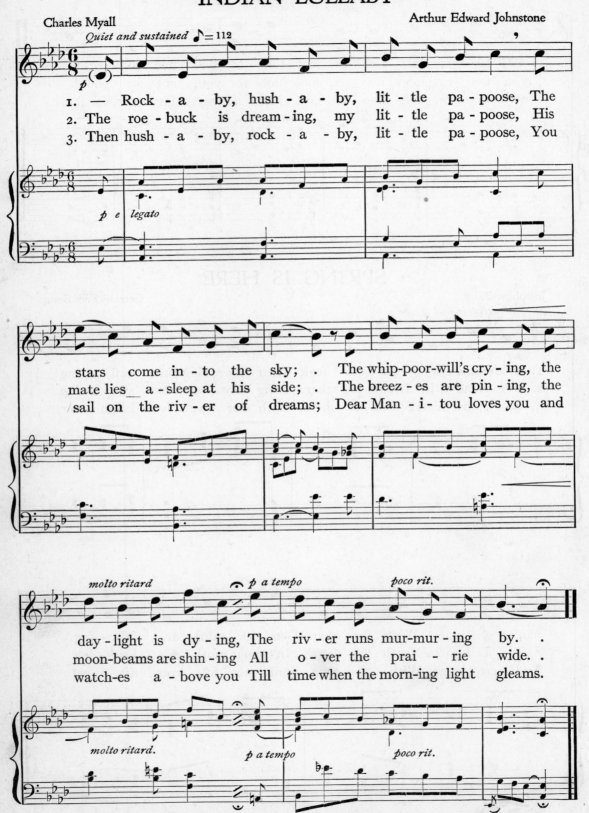

Quiet and sustained ♪ = 112

1. — Rock - a - by, hush - a - by, lit - tle pa - poose, The
2. The roe - buck is dream - ing, my lit - tle pa - poose, His
3. Then hush - a - by, rock - a - by, lit - tle pa - poose, You

stars come in - to the sky; . The whip-poor-will's cry - ing, the
mate lies a - sleep at his side; . The breez - es are pin - ing, the
sail on the riv - er of dreams; Dear Man - i - tou loves you and

day - light is dy - ing, The riv - er runs mur-mur - ing by. .
moon-beams are shin - ing All o - ver the prai - rie wide. .
watch - es a - bove you Till time when the morn-ing light gleams.

GIVING THANKS
(MAGDALENA)

German Traditional Melody

Andantino ♩.= 50

We thank thee, lov - ing Fa - ther, For all thy ten - der care,

For food and clothes and shel - ter And all the world so fair.

HEAR THE WIND!

J. L. V.

J. Lilian Vandevere

Moderato ♩ = 69

1. The au - tumn wind goes round a - bout. Oo! . . . . . Oo!
2. The au - tumn wind goes high and low. Oo! . . . . . Oo!

. . . . . . On frost - y nights you hear it shout, Oo! .
. . . . . . We shiv - er when we hear it blow, Oo! .

. . . . . . It says, "The nights are long - er." It says, "The cold is
. . . . . . Its voice is wild and gust - y, Its tune is loud and

strong - er, And win - ter's ver - y near, no doubt." Oo! . . . . . .
lust - y; It makes us think of com - ing snow. Oo! . . . . . .

BROTHER, COME AND DANCE

English version by Melissa Murphy

German Folk Song
Used by Humperdinck in "Hänsel and Gretel"

(Girls) 1. Broth-er, come and dance with me   Un-der-neath the ap-ple tree;
(Boys) 2. Sis-ter, I will dance with you   If you'll tell me what to do,
(Girls) 3. Broth-er, I have shown you how;   Let us dance to-geth-er now;

D.C. 3rd stanza

Make a bow, Nice-ly, now! Come and let me show you how!
How to go To and fro With the mu-sic, fast and slow.
Heel and toe, Right foot so, Turn a-bout and off we go!

BUMBLEBEE AND CLOVER

From "The Children's First Book of Poetry"
Emilie Kip Baker

Henry Fisher

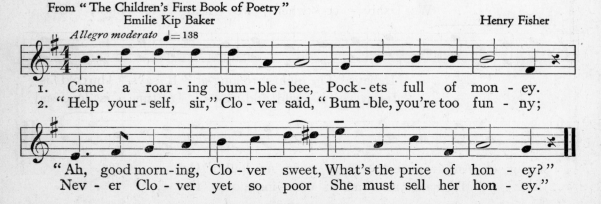

1. Came a roar-ing bum-ble-bee, Pock-ets full of mon-ey.
2. "Help your-self, sir," Clo-ver said, "Bum-ble, you're too fun-ny;

"Ah, good morn-ing, Clo-ver sweet, What's the price of hon-ey?"
Nev-er Clo-ver yet so poor She must sell her hon-ey."

THE WIND

Robert Louis Stevenson

Clarence Butler

1. I saw you toss the kites on high And blow the birds a - bout the sky;
2. I saw the dif-f'rent things you did, But al - ways you yourself you hid.
3. O you that are so strong and cold, O blow - er, are you young or old?

And all a-round I heard you pass, Like la-dies' skirts a-cross the grass;
I felt you push, I heard you call, I could not see your-self at all;
Are you a beast of field and tree, Or just a strong-er child than me?

O wind, a - blow - ing all day long, O wind, that sings so loud a song!
O wind, a - blow - ing all day long, O wind, that sings so loud a song!
O wind, a - blow - ing all day long, O wind, that sings so loud a song!

THE THREE SQUIRRELS

Melissa Murphy

French Folk Tune

Lively ♩. = 63

1. Three, three, three lit - tle squir - rels, Gray, gray, gray as can be,
2. "Oh, oh, oh, we are hun - gry! What, what, what shall we eat?"
3. "Look! look! day - light is go - ing! Now, now, day - light is fled!

Live, live, live with their moth - er, Deep, deep, deep in a tree.
"Here, here, here is an a - corn, Yum, yum, yum - my and sweet.
Oh, oh, oh, we are sleep - y! Come, come, let's go to bed!"

Out in the morn - ing they run with glee, Leap - ing and play - ing
Here is an a - corn or two or three! Search and you'll find them
Back to their moth - er they run, all three, Read - y for slum - ber,

Ped.

under the branch - es, Out in the morn - ing they
un - der the branch - es, Here is an a - corn or
read - y for sleep - ing, Back to their moth - er they

Ped.

run with glee, Leap - ing and play - ing un - der the tree.
two or three! Search and you'll find them un - der the tree."
run, all three, Read - y for slum - ber, deep in the tree.

DOCTOR FOSTER

English text by Lydia Foote

French Folk Song

Allegro ♩. = 66

1. Doc - tor Fos - ter's sail - ing a - way O - ver the chan - nel so
2. Fare you well, you jol - ly old man, Safe be your jour - ney and

rough and so storm - y; Doc - tor Fos - ter's sail - ing a - way
safe be your land - ing; Fare you well, you jol - ly old man,

O - ver the chan - nel and o - ver the bay.
Come back to see us when - ev - er you can.

LOVELY APRIL

Anthony Gillespie

German Folk Song

With spirit ♩ = 88

mp

1. Love - ly A - pril is a maid so free, Sing - ing mag - ic songs of
2. Buds are burst-ing on the wil - low spray! Lambs are skip-ping to the
3. To the breeze your care and sor - row fling, All the earth and air are

mf cresc - - en - - do

mirth and glee,— "Come you, come you, come you,
fields a - way! "Come you, come you, come you,
full of spring! "Come you, come you, come you,

pp (echo)   *f poco rit.*

Come you, come you, come you, Come out with me!"
Come you, come you, come you, Come out and play!"
Come you, come you, come you, Come out and sing!"

THE KNIFE GRINDER

L. F.

Lydia Foote

Maids and wives, maids and wives, Here I come to sharpen your knives; Maids and

wives, maids and wives, Here I come to sharp-en your knives. Now you can

cut your bread and meat, And give your fam-i-ly sup-per to eat; Now you can

cut your bread and meat and give your fam-i-ly sup-per to eat. Maids and

OH, DEAR! WHAT CAN THE MATTER BE?

English Tune

Oh, dear! what can the mat-ter be? Dear, dear!
what can the mat-ter be? Oh, dear! what can the mat-ter be?
John-ny's so long at the Fair. . . Fair. .

1. He prom-ised to buy me a bunch of blue rib-bons, He
2. He prom-ised he'd bring me a bas-ket of po-sies, A

cresc - - - en - - - do

prom - ised to buy me a bunch of blue rib - bons, He
gar - land of lil - ies, a gar - land of ros - es, A

prom - ised to buy me a bunch of blue rib - bons, To
lit - tle straw hat to set off the blue rib - bons That

tie up my bon - ny brown hair. . . And it's
tie up my bon - ny brown hair. . . And it's

TEN MILES FROM HOME

(HIKING SONG)

Anon.   Old English Folk Tune

Allegro moderato ♩ = 92

1. We're ten miles from home, We're ten miles from home; We
2. We're nine miles from home, We're nine miles from home; We

walk a mile, we rest a while, We're nine miles from home.
walk a mile, we rest a while, We're eight miles from home.*

*Continue — Eight miles, seven miles, etc.   Last stanza, And now we're at home.

WHEN THE LITTLE CHILDREN SLEEP

Carl Reinecke

When the lit - tle chil - dren sleep, Lit - tle stars are wak - ing;

An - gels bright from heav - en come, And, till morn is break - ing,

They will watch the live - long night By their beds till morn - ing light.

When the lit - tle chil - dren sleep, Stars and an - gels watch do keep.

GARDENS IN THE SEA

Manx Folk Tune

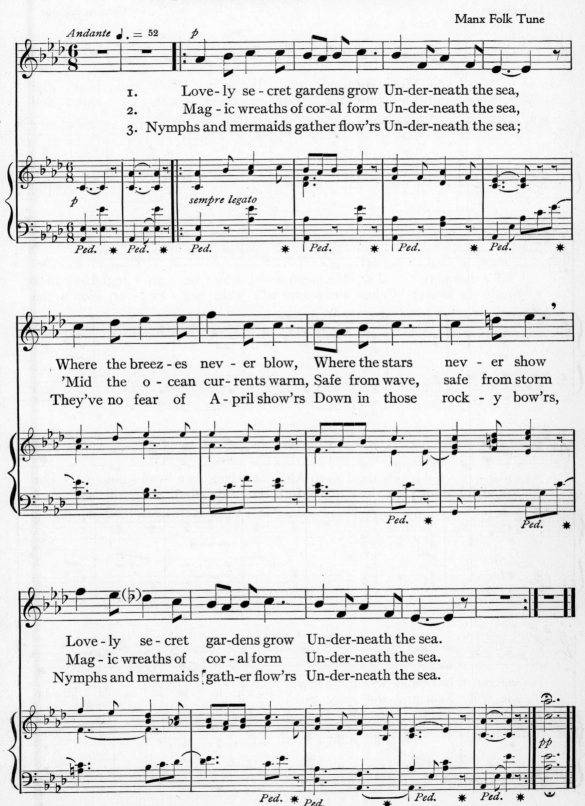

Andante ♩. = 52

1. Love-ly se-cret gardens grow Un-der-neath the sea,
2. Mag-ic wreaths of cor-al form Un-der-neath the sea,
3. Nymphs and mermaids gather flow'rs Un-der-neath the sea;

Where the breez-es nev-er blow, Where the stars nev-er show
'Mid the o-cean cur-rents warm, Safe from wave, safe from storm
They've no fear of A-pril show'rs Down in those rock-y bow'rs,

Love-ly se-cret gar-dens grow Un-der-neath the sea.
Mag-ic wreaths of cor-al form Un-der-neath the sea.
Nymphs and mermaids gath-er flow'rs Un-der-neath the sea.

WORK AND PLAY

Lydia Foote

German Melody

la la la la la la la la la la la la la la la la.

MORNING HYMN

Maxwell Gaddis

Latvian Hymn Tune

Maestoso ♩ = 92

mf

mf *legato*

1. Come, let us now up-raise Voic - es in joy - ful praise, Praise to the
2. Faith - ful, the gold - en sun, Ris - ing, his course to run, Shines on the

Lord of Lords in Heav - en a - bove. Come thou to earth be - low,
wait-ing earth from Heav - en a - bove. Lord, thou more faith - ful art,

f

Make us thy ways to know, Fill thou our hearts, O God, whose name is Love.
Shin - ing with-in my heart, Time - less and true, O God, whose name is Love.

TWO SONGS

Ira Barton

Ira Barton

1. The herds-man by the rock - y shore He sang an an - cient lay—
2. The sail - or sang an an - cient song Come down from days of yore—

Ah! And
Ah! And

o - ver the wa - ter there came to him an an - swer from the
o - ver the wa - ter there came to him an an - swer from the

bay.
shore. Ah!

CURLY LOCKS AND THE CHESTNUT MAN

Ira Barton

Melissa Murphy

1. "Chest-nut man! Chest-nut man! I've a gold-en pen-ny; You have chest-nuts

2. "Curl - y Locks, Curl-y Locks! Keep your shin-ing gold; Here are chest-nuts

pip-ing hot; Will you sell me an - y?"

pip-ing-hot, All your hands can hold!"

GOOD NIGHT!

Mrs. A. D. Willard

F. J. Hatton

List to the bells in the stee - ple, Call-ing a - far to the peo - ple. "Good night, ding—dong, good night, ding—dong, good night, ding—dong, good night!" While close to your bed, as they're ring - ing, Your own lov - ing moth - er is sing - ing:

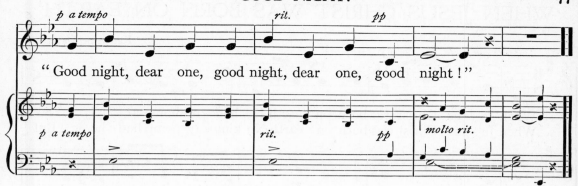

p a tempo   *rit.*   *pp*

"Good night, dear one, good night, dear one, good night!"

p a tempo   *rit.*   *pp*   *molto rit.*

O MY DEAR HEART

Anonymous   Katherine Davis

Andante con moto ♩ = 108

1. O my dear heart, young Je - sus blest, Pre - pare thy cra - dle
2. Then ev - er - more my voice I'll raise In sweet - est songs un -

in . my breast; And I shall rock thee in . my heart, And
to . thy praise. My heart shall bow with bend - ed knee, And

nev - er-more from thee de - part, And nev - er-more from thee de - part.
lull - a - by I'll sing to thee, And lull - a - by I'll sing to thee.

poco rall.

WHEN JESUS CHRIST WAS BORN ON EARTH

Katherine Davis

AN AIR RIDE

N. Grier Parke

Arthur Edward Johnstone

1. Swing, swing in - to the sky, We're leav-ing the fields be - low us;
2. High, high up thro' the air So swift-ly our way we're wing - ing;

Wing, wing, fly - ing so high, The swal-lows are there to show us.
Sky, sky, o - cean so fair, Our ship to your shores we're bring -ing.

Low, low, near to the ground, Then rise, rise, Sky-ward we're bound, So
Sail, sail, o - ver the moon, Then turn, turn home a - gain soon, And

smooth and swift-ly we sail a - long, The winds of Sep-tem - ber blow us.
oh, the sto - ry that we can tell Of lands where we went a-swing-ing!

CRADLE SONG

English text by K. D.

Wolfgang Amadeus Mozart

1. Sleep, O my lit - tle one, sleep, Fold - ed in qui - et so deep.
2. Sleep, O my lit - tle one, sleep, Nought breaks the qui - et so deep.

Now are the lil - y and rose Drows-ing in dew - y re - pose;
Here in the shad-ow - y house Si - lent are crick-et and mouse;

Soft - ly the moon with her light Shad-ows the sil - ver - y
O - ver your slum-ber - ing head Heav - en - ly wings are out -

night; Fold - ed in qui - et so deep,
spread. Nought breaks the qui - et so deep,

Sleep, O my lit-tle one, Sleep. O sleep, ... O

sleep. . sleep! .

BOY AND BIRD

Ira Barton

Canadian Folk Song

With spirit ♩ = 63

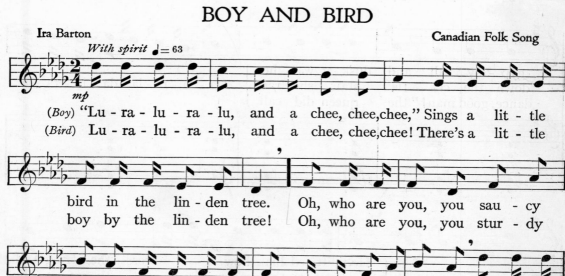

(Boy) "Lu - ra - lu - ra - lu, and a chee, chee, chee," Sings a lit - tle
(Bird) Lu - ra - lu - ra - lu, and a chee, chee, chee! There's a lit - tle

bird in the lin - den tree. Oh, who are you, you sau - cy
boy by the lin - den tree! Oh, who are you, you stur - dy

fel - low, Swing-ing on the bough with your wings of yel - low? Say, will you
fel - low? Ros - y are your cheeks and your hair is yel - low. Why don't you

sing once more for me? "Lu - ra - lu - ra - lu - ra, and a chee, chee, chee!"
come and fly with me? Lu - ra - lu - ra - lu - ra, and a chee, chee, chee!

THE QUEEN DANCES

Katherine Davis

K. D.

Not too fast ♩. = 60

1. The fid - dler stood 'neath the
2. The queen looked out on the
3. A beg - gar stopped by the

lin - den tree,
gyp - sy man,
cas - tle wall,

Da - la - ra - la, da - la - ra - la dum dum dum dee

A
Then
"Come

gyp - sy tall and dusk - y was he.
down the cas - tle stair she ran.
dance, good man!" the queen did call.

Da - la - ra - la, da - la - ra - la

dum dum dum dee!

He lift - ed his bow a - cross the string And
And out to the court be - neath the moon, The
And so . they danced to the gyp - sy tune, The

mer - ry and light the fid - dle did sing!
bet - ter to hear the gyp - sy tune. } Da - la - ra - la, da - la - ra - la,
beg - gar and queen be - neath the moon! }

da - la - ra - la dee! Sing Da - la - ra - la, da - la - ra - la dum dum dum dee!

HEAR OUR CALL

English translation by Lydia Foote

German Folk Song

Gayly ♩ = 88

1. Hear our call! Hear our call, hear our call, To the mead- ow
2. Life glows bright! Life glows bright, steps are light, Youth's the time when

come you all! No de - lay! Haste a - way! Now's the time for play!
all is right! Hearts so gay, Blithe as May, Join the roun - de - lay.

If you do not care to come, Lock your door and stay at home,
If you take no joy in song, Sad you'll be your whole life long.

While we sing, Dance and spring, Till the ech - oes ring!
There - fore sing! Dance and spring Till the ech - oes ring!

THE GOLDEN CAROL

(OF MELCHIOR, BALTHAZER, AND CASPAR)

Old English

Joyfully ♩. = 60

1. We saw a light shine out a - far, On Christ-mas in the morn - ing, And
2. O ev - 'ry thought be of his Name, On Christ-mas in the morn - ing, Who

straight we knew it was Christ's star Bright beam-ing in the morn - ing. Then
bore for us both grief and shame, Af - flic - tions sharp - est scorn - ing. And

did we fall on bend - ed knee, On Christ-mas in the morn - ing, And
may we die (when death shall come) On Christ-mas in the morn - ing, And

praised the Lord, who'd let us see His glo - ry at its dawn - ing.
see in heav'n, our glo - rious home, That Star of Christ-mas morn - ing.

WHEN MARY LULLED HER BABE TO SLEEP

Katherine Davis

Austrian Carol

1. When Mary lulled her Babe to sleep On holy Christmas night, . . A-bove the man-ger where he lay There shone a won-drous light, . . There shone a wondrous light. . . .

2. The bless-ed light that shone that night Still shines on earth to-day, . . And all who move in peace and love May see its gold-en ray, . . May see its gold-en ray. . . .

3. O Je-sus sweet, so small thou art, Yet great thy power must be, . . For thou to-day hast filled my heart With ten-der love for thee, . . With ten-der love for thee. . . .

SANTA CLAUS

N. Grier Parke

Arthur Edward Johnstone

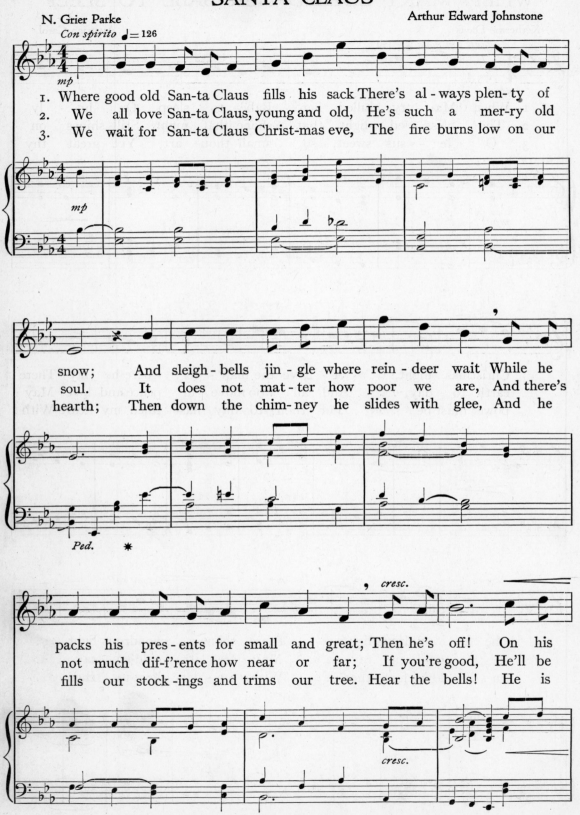

1. Where good old San-ta Claus fills his sack There's al-ways plen-ty of
2. We all love San-ta Claus, young and old, He's such a mer-ry old
3. We wait for San-ta Claus Christ-mas eve, The fire burns low on our

snow; And sleigh-bells jin-gle where rein-deer wait While he
soul. It does not mat-ter how poor we are, And there's
hearth; Then down the chim-ney he slides with glee, And he

packs his pres-ents for small and great; Then he's off! On his
not much dif-f'rence how near or far; If you're good, He'll be
fills our stock-ings and trims our tree. Hear the bells! He is

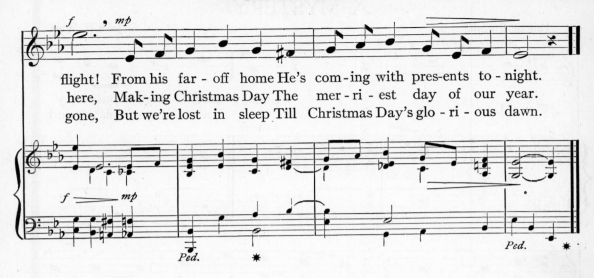

flight! From his far - off home He's com - ing with pres-ents to - night.
here, Mak-ing Christmas Day The mer - ri - est day of our year.
gone, But we're lost in sleep Till Christmas Day's glo - ri - ous dawn.

NEW EVERY MORNING IS THY LOVE
(CANONBURY)

Rev. John Keble

Robert Schumann

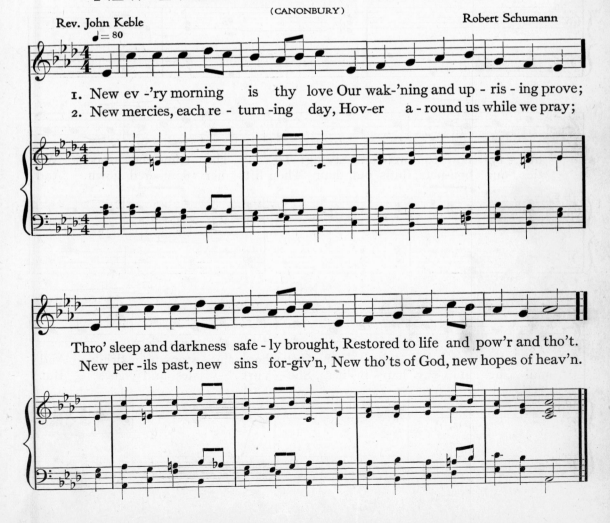

1. New ev -'ry morning is thy love Our wak-'ning and up - ris - ing prove;
2. New mercies, each re - turn -ing day, Hov-er a - round us while we pray;

Thro' sleep and darkness safe - ly brought, Restored to life and pow'r and tho't.
New per -ils past, new sins for-giv'n, New tho'ts of God, new hopes of heav'n.

A MYSTERY

Pauline Cushing

John E. West

*Small notes with second stanza.

find a mir-ror in the brook; We'll stand up-on the brink..
why she comes but once a year, No long-ing puss-y knows..

2. She

MY SERVANTS

Translated by Ira Barton

German Folk Song

Allegro ♪ = 152

1. Pe - ter— Pe - ter Perk - ey I call my pet tur - key.
2. Pe - ter— Pe - ter Perk - ey I call my pet tur - key.
3. Pe - ter— Pe - ter Perk - ey I call my pet tur - key.

Can't - run - quick, that is my chick, Bump - on - a - log,
Out - of - luck, that is my duck, Vel - vet - hat,
Shag - gy - coat, that is my goat, Delve - and - dig,

that is my dog. Pe - ter— Pe - ter Perk - ey I call my pet tur - key.
that is my cat. Pe - ter— Pe - ter Perk - ey I call my pet tur - key.
that is my pig. Pe - ter— Pe - ter Perk - ey I call my pet tur - key.

NIGHT AND DAY

Mary Mapes Dodge

Samuel P. Warren

1. When I run a-bout all day, When I kneel at night to pray, God sees,

God sees. 2. When I'm dreaming in the dark, When I lie a-wake and hark,

God sees, God sees. 3. Need I ev-er know a fear? Night and day my

Fa-ther's near; God sees, God sees. . .

SPRING RAIN

THE SEASONS

Burton Egbert Stevenson

Arthur Edward Johnstone

SPRING AND WINTER

Moderato ♩ = 108

1. March brings breezes, loud and shrill, To stir the dancing daf - fo - dil.
4. Chill De - cem - ber brings the sleet, Blaz - ing fire and Christ - mas treat.

A - pril brings the prim - rose sweet, Scat - ters dais - ies at our feet.
Jan - u - a - ry brings the snow, Makes our feet and fin - gers glow.

May brings flocks of pret - ty lambs, Skip - ping by their fleec - y dams.
Feb - ru - a - ry brings the rain, Thaws the fro - zen lake a - gain.

SUMMER

2. June brings tu - lips, lil - ies, ros - es, Fills the chil - dren's hands with pos - ies.

Hot Ju - ly brings cool-ing show-ers, A - pri-cots and gil - ly flow-ers.

August brings the sheaves of corn, Then the har-vest home is borne.

AUTUMN

mp

3. Warm Sep-tem - ber brings the fruit; Sports-men then be - gin to shoot.

Fresh Oc - to - ber brings the pheas-ant; Then to gath - er nuts is pleas-ant.

HDI—7

Dull No-vem-ber brings the blast; Then the leaves are whirl-ing fast.

THE LOTUS FLOWER

K. D.

Chinese Melody

Lightly ♩ = 92

1. Lean - ing last night . from my win - dow so high,
2. Now, in my gar - den in the dark si - lent pool,

I saw a star fall . down from the sky; Swift it sped in a
There blooms a lo - tus flow-er, fra - grant and cool; Soft she glows with a

glow of light, Slid thro' the air and was lost from my sight.
pale gold light, Shin - ing and fair as a star in the night.

ONCE IN ROYAL DAVID'S CITY
(IRBY)

Mrs. Cecil Frances Alexander

Henry J. Gauntlett

1. Once in roy - al Da - vid's cit - y Stood a low - ly cat - tle shed,
2. And thro' all his won-drous child-hood He would hon - or and o - bey,

Where a moth - er laid her Ba - by In a man - ger for his bed;
Love and watch the low - ly maid - en In whose gen - tle arms he lay;

Ma - ry was that moth-er mild; Je - sus Christ, her lit - tle Child.
Chris-tian chil - dren all must be Mild, o - be - dient, good as he.

A PRAYER

W. A. Mozart

1. As the sun doth dai - ly rise, Bright-'ning all the morn-ing skies,
2. When the sun with-draws his light, When we seek our beds at night,

So to thee with one ac - cord Lift we up our hearts, O Lord!
Thou, by sleep-less hosts a - dored, Hear the pray'r of faith, O Lord!

TWO SONGS FROM
"A CHILD'S GARDEN OF VERSES"

I. BED IN SUMMER

Robert Louis Stevenson

Ethelbert Nevin

Allegretto scherzando (*Tempo rubato*)

In win-ter I get up at night And dress by yel-low can-dle light; In sum-mer quite the oth-er way, I have to go to bed by day. I have to go to bed and see The birds still hop-ping

II. SINGING

Ethelbert Nevin

THE BARLEY MOW

Ann White

Ann White

Con moto

Now's the time for the bar-ley mow, The bar-ley mow, the bar-ley mow;

Now's the time for the bar-ley mow When the dew is on the grass. grass.

Up and o-ver the fields we go, The fields we go, the fields we go;

Up and o-ver the fields we go, Each mer-ry lad and lass.

D.C. al Fine

TULIPS

J. Lilian Vandevere

John E. West

Last fall I plant-ed tu-lips; I tucked them safe-ly down, And ev-'ry sin-gle tu-lip bulb Wore o-ver-alls of brown. 2. This East-er-time they blos-somed, And what do you sup-pose? Each love-ly lit-tle

tu - lip flow'r Wore yel - low sat - in clothes!

FOREIGN CHILDREN

Robert Louis Stevenson*

Russian Folk Song

1. Lit - tle In - dian, Sioux or Crow, Lit - tle frost - y Es - ki - mo,
2. You have seen the scar - let trees And the li - ons o - ver - seas;
3. Such a life is ver - y fine, But it's not so nice as mine;

Lit - tle Turk or Jap - a - nee, Oh, don't you wish that you were me?
You have eat - en os - trich eggs, And turn'd the tur - tles off their legs.
You must of - ten, as you trod, Have wear - ied *not* to be a - broad.

4. You have curious things to eat,
   I am fed on proper meat;
   You must dwell beyond the foam,
   But I am safe and live at home.

5. Little Indian, Sioux or Crow,
   Little frosty Eskimo,
   Little Turk or Japanee,
   Oh, don't you wish that you were me?

*Used by permission of Charles Scribner's Sons, owners of the copyright.

CARPENTER, CARPENTER

Ann White

Ann White

Not too fast ♩ = 120

1. Car - pen - ter, car - pen - ter, how . do you do?
2. Car - pen - ter, car - pen - ter, ham-mer down the floor!

Build me a cot - tage just big e-nough for two, Or
Set in the win-dows and swing . up the door; Please

may - be I'd like it just big e-nough for three—
lay on the shin - gles as quick as quick can be,

cresc - - en - - do poco rit.

Big e-nough for dad - dy and moth - er and me.
Read - y for dad - dy and moth - er and me.

GOLDEN SLUMBERS

Thomas Dekker
From "Patient Grisel"

English Lullaby of
Seventeenth Century

Andante ♩ = 126

1. Gold - en slum-bers kiss your eyes, Smiles a - wait you when you rise;
2. 'Neath the drow-sy droop-ing lid, Dreams from fair - y land are hid;

p e legato

Sleep, pret-ty lov'd one, do not cry And I will sing you lull - a - by,
Sleep, pret-ty lov'd one, do not cry And I will sing you lull - a - by,

lull - a - by, lull - a - by, lull - a - by. . .

Ped.

LADY-LADY

M. M.

Melissa Murphy

Allegretto ♩ = 76

La - dy, la - dy, buy a broom for your ba - by! Sweep him low and

1st *2d*

sweep him high, and sweep the cob-webs out of the sky! out of the sky!

AN EASTER CAROL

Emily D. Chapman

Leopold Damrosch

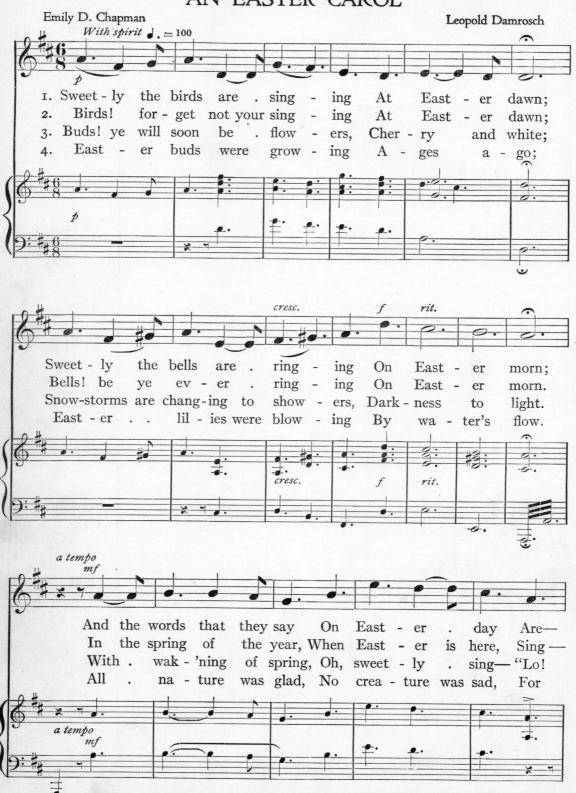

1. Sweet-ly the birds are . sing - ing At East-er dawn;
2. Birds! for-get not your sing - ing At East-er dawn;
3. Buds! ye will soon be . flow-ers, Cher-ry and white;
4. East-er buds were grow-ing A - ges a-go;

Sweet-ly the bells are . ring - ing On East-er morn;
Bells! be ye ev-er . ring - ing On East-er morn.
Snow-storms are chang-ing to show-ers, Dark-ness to light.
East-er . . lil-ies were blow-ing By wa-ter's flow.

And the words that they say On East-er . day Are—
In the spring of the year, When East-er is here, Sing—
With . wak-'ning of spring, Oh, sweet-ly . sing— "Lo!
All . na-ture was glad, No crea-ture was sad, For

From *St. Nicholas Songs.* Used by permission of the publishers, D. Appleton-Century Co., Inc.

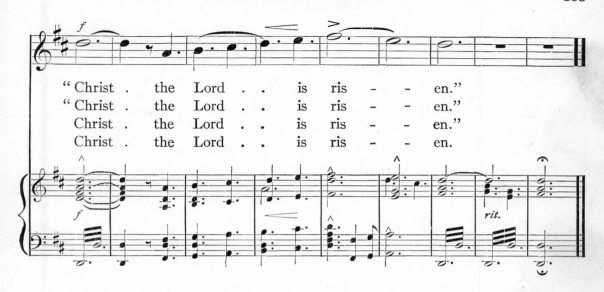

"Christ . the Lord . . is ris - - en."
"Christ . the Lord . . is ris - - en."
Christ . the Lord . . is ris - - en.
Christ . the Lord . . is ris - - en.

ON OLD NORTH BRIDGE

Translation by Anthony Gillespie

French Folk Song

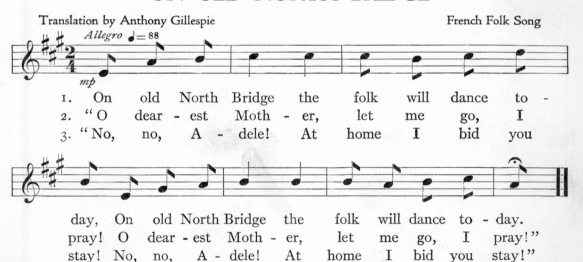

Allegro ♩ = 88

mp

1. On old North Bridge the folk will dance to -
2. "O dear - est Moth - er, let me go, I
3. "No, no, A - dele! At home I bid you

day, On old North Bridge the folk will dance to - day.
pray! O dear - est Moth - er, let me go, I pray!"
stay! No, no, A - dele! At home I bid you stay!"

4. She starts to cry and sadly turns away.   (twice)
5. Her brother comes a-rowing o'er the bay.   (twice)
6. "Why do you weep, O Sister? Tell me, pray!"   (twice)
7. "Because at home my mother bade me stay!"   (twice)
8. "Put on your dress with ribbons red and gay!"   (twice)
9. So off they go, a-rowing o'er the bay.   (twice)
10. They danced but once, then in the water fell.   (twice)
11. And so were drowned, as quick as tongue can tell.   (twice)
12. Their mother said, "Why tolls the village bell?"   (twice)
13. "'Tis for your oldest son and for Adele."   (twice)
14. Such things as this may happen any day
   To naughty children who will not obey.   (twice)

THE ANGEL

Adapted from the German by K. D.

German Folk Song

1. There came a shin-ing an-gel And stood be-side my bed; A-
2. Then thro' the dark he whis-pered And told me not to fear. "I
3. He spoke, and seemed to van-ish, But when the night was gone, And

cross the pur-ple dark-ness His gold-en wings he spread. His
am your guard-ian an-gel And I am al-ways near. When
forth I went at morn-ing, I went no more a-lone. And

eyes were calm and glow-ing, His hair was like a flame; And
you have learned to trust me, Be-side you I shall stand, And
though I can-not see him I feel his pres-ence near; In

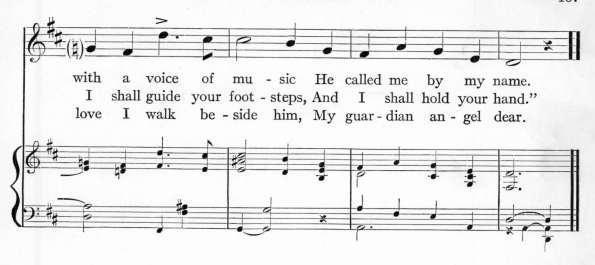

with   a   voice   of   mu - sic   He   called   me   by   my   name.
I   shall   guide   your   foot - steps,   And   I   shall   hold   your   hand."
love   I   walk   be - side   him,   My   guar - dian   an - gel   dear.

THE EVENING STAR

English version by K. D.

Robert Schumann

1. The   bright   eve - ning   star   Looks   down   from   a - far   And
2. I   look   up   to   see   How   bright   she   may   be,   And
3. And   al - ways   her   light   Gives   calm   to   the   night;   I

greets   us   with   shin - ing   Wher - ev - er   we   are.
al - ways   in   an - swer   She   looks   back   at   me.
wish   I   were   like   her,   So   peace - ful,   so   bright.

WILLY-WILLY-WILL

Arranged by Johannes Brahms for
Robert and Clara Schumann's children

1. Wil - ly - Wil - ly - Will, The Ped - dler's com - ing;
2. Wil - ly - Wil - ly - Will, The Ped - dler car - ries,
3. Wil - ly - Wil - ly - Will, The Ped - dler car - ries,
4. Wil - ly - Wil - ly - Will, The Ped - dler's com - ing,

Wil-ly-Wil-ly-Will, What's in his pack? Wil-ly-Wil-ly-Will, Some
Wil-ly-Wil-ly-Will, A good stiff rule, Wil-ly-Wil-ly-Will, For
Wil-ly-Wil-ly-Will, A dose to take, Wil-ly-Wil-ly-Will, For
Wil-ly-Wil-ly-Will, But not for me, Wil-ly-Wil-ly-Will, For

nuts and rai - sins, Wil - ly-Wil - ly-Will, And can-dy in a sack.
boys who lin - ger, Wil - ly-Wil - ly-Will, Up - on the way to school.
hun - gry fel - lows, Wil - ly-Wil - ly-Will, Who stole their moth-er's cake.
I am be - ing, Wil - ly-Wil - ly-Will, As good as I can be!

AN EASTER SECRET

J. Lilian Vandevere

Arthur Archer

Moderato ♩ = 88

1. The sun-shine told the rob-in, The rob-in told a bee, The
2. The breeze be-gan to whis-per, The trees be-gan to talk, The

bee be-gan his hum-ming, And he whis-pered it to me.
hop-toad took the mes-sage, Up and down the gar-den walk.

What do you sup-pose? Lis-ten while I tell—
You'll be so sur-prised, Come and see it, too—

Here's an East-er chick-en That has bro-ken from his shell!
Here's an East-er tu-lip That is bloom-ing just for you!

poco rit.

AN APRIL GIRL

Mary Mapes Dodge

J. Remington Fairlamb

1. The girl that's born on an
2. The girls of March love
3. Heigh-ho! hur - rah! for an

A - pril day Has a right to be mer - ry, . light-some, gay; And
noise and fray, And sweet as . blos-soms are girls of May; But
A - pril day, Its . cloud, its . spar - kle, its skip and stay! I

that is the rea - son I dance and play, And frisk like a mote in a
I re - joice in a sun - ny spray Of smiles and tears and
mean to be hap - py when-ev - er I may, And cry when I must, for .

From *St. Nicholas Songs.* Used by permission of the publishers, D. Appleton-Century Co., Inc.

sun - ny ray,—Would-n't you Do it too, If you had been born on an
hap - a - day,—Would-n't you Do it too, If you had been born on an
that's my way. Would-n't you Do it too, If you had been born on an

A - pril day, If you had been born on an A - pril day?
A - pril day, If you had been born on an A - pril day?
A - pril day, If you had been born on an A - pril day?

IN ORCHARD GREEN

Lydia Foote

Wenzel Müller

Slowly ♩. = 72

1. In or - chard green there stands a tree, As white as
2. Bend down your boughs, O or - chard tree, With crim - son
3. A - lone you stand, O or - chard tree; No fra - grant

snow, as fair to see. With A - pril wind the blos - soms
birds so fair to see. Sep - tem - ber comes, the ap - ples
bloom, no fruit I see. De - cem - ber snows a - bout you

fly And on the grass the pet - als lie.
fall, The crim - son birds have van - ished all.
cling, But still you sleep and dream of spring.

WINTER WIND

J. L. V.

German Folk Song

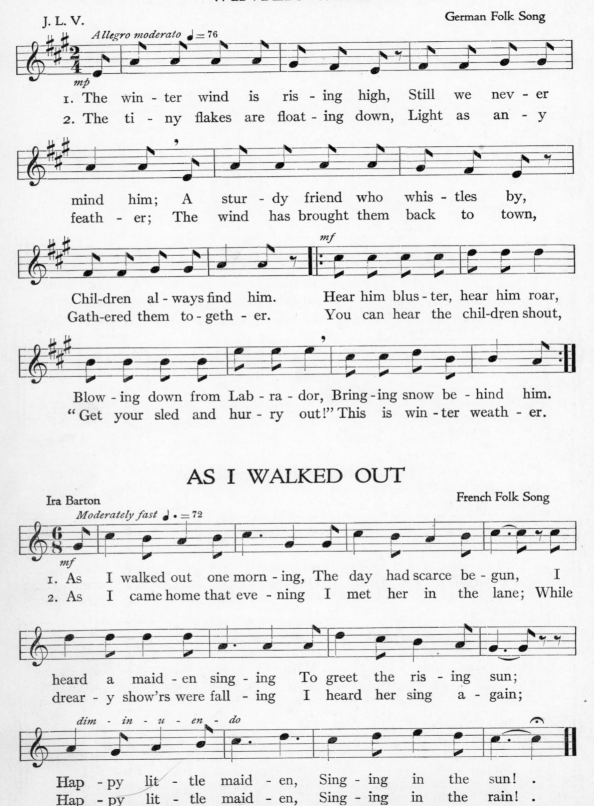

Allegro moderato ♩ = 76

mp

1. The win-ter wind is ris-ing high, Still we nev-er
2. The ti-ny flakes are float-ing down, Light as an-y

mind him; A stur-dy friend who whis-tles by,
feath-er; The wind has brought them back to town,

mf

Chil-dren al-ways find him. Hear him blus-ter, hear him roar,
Gath-ered them to-geth-er. You can hear the chil-dren shout,

Blow-ing down from Lab-ra-dor, Bring-ing snow be-hind him.
"Get your sled and hur-ry out!" This is win-ter weath-er.

AS I WALKED OUT

Ira Barton

French Folk Song

Moderately fast ♩• = 72

mf

1. As I walked out one morn-ing, The day had scarce be-gun, I
2. As I came home that eve-ning I met her in the lane; While

heard a maid-en sing-ing To greet the ris-ing sun;
drear-y show'rs were fall-ing I heard her sing a-gain;

dim-in-u-en-do

Hap-py lit-tle maid-en, Sing-ing in the sun! .
Hap-py lit-tle maid-en, Sing-ing in the rain! .

UP AND DOWN THE SHADY LANE

Ann White

Ann White

Not too fast ♩. = 60

mf

1. Up and down the shad - y lane I saw the pip - er go,
2. Up and down the shad - y lane I saw the chil - dren go,

Play - ing all the mer - ry tunes The vil - lage chil - dren know.
Danc - ing to the mu - sic that The mer - ry pipes did blow.

f

Play - ing all the sum - mer day, Mak - ing mu - sic loud and gay—
Danc - ing all the sum - mer day, To the mu - sic loud and gay—

rall.

a tempo

mp

Up and down the shad - y lane I saw the pip - er go.
Up and down the shad - y lane I saw the chil - dren go.

COSSACK'S LULLABY

Translation Anon.

Melody by N. Bachmetieff

1. Sleep, ah, sleep, my dar - ling ba - by, Su, su, lull - a - by; . .
2. All too soon wilt thou be learn - ing Of a war - rior's life; . .
3. Keep this tal - is - man I give thee In re - membrance dear. . .

See, the moon is watch-ing o'er thee, Peace-ful - ly on high. . .
With the gun and pranc-ing war-horse, Mov-ing to the strife. . .
May it thro' thy life pro - tect thee When dark dan-ger's near. . .

Thou shalt hear a won-drous sto - ry, Close each wake-ful eye; . .
Sad - dle, bri - dle, all, my ba - by, Shalt thou by and by. . .
Think of me when thou dost see it, Pray to God on high; . .

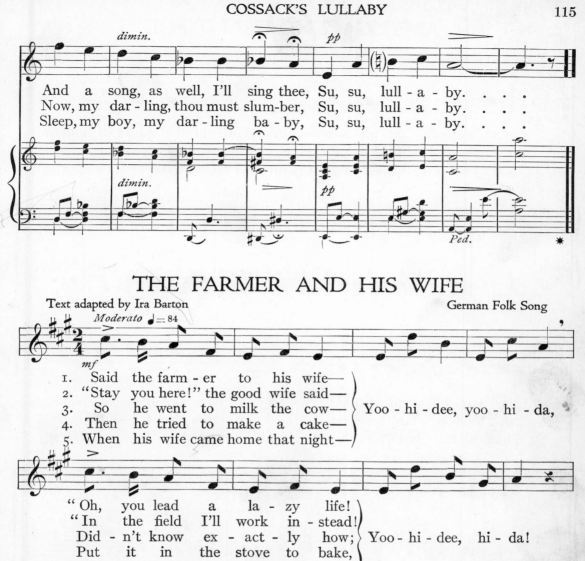

dimin.   *pp*

And   a   song, as   well, I'll   sing thee, Su, su,   lull - a - by. . . .
Now, my   dar - ling, thou must slum - ber, Su, su,   lull - a - by. . . .
Sleep, my boy, my   dar - ling   ba - by,   Su, su,   lull - a - by. . . .

dimin.

pp   *Ped.*

THE FARMER AND HIS WIFE

Text adapted by Ira Barton   German Folk Song

Moderato ♩ = 84

mf

1. Said   the farm - er   to   his wife—
2. "Stay   you here!" the good wife said—
3. So   he went to   milk   the   cow— } Yoo - hi - dee, yoo - hi - da,
4. Then   he tried to   make   a   cake—
5. When   his wife came home that night—

"Oh,   you lead   a   la - zy   life!
"In   the field   I'll   work   in - stead!
Did - n't know   ex - act - ly   how; } Yoo - hi - dee,   hi - da!
Put   it   in   the   stove   to   bake,
Farm - er   was   a   sor - ry   sight!

Here be - side the hearth you stay Close   at home the   live - long day!"
I   shall go   and   run   the plough, You may stay   and milk the cow!"
Bos - sie thought, "You clum - sy lout!" Spilled the milk and kicked him out!
Ne'er - the - less,   for   all   his   care, Burned him - self both here and there!
"Wife," said he, "To - mor - row day Here   at home I   beg you stay!"

mf cresc - - - en - - do

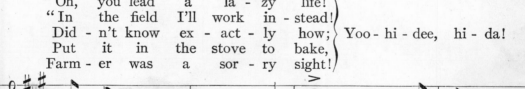

Yoo - hi - dee   hi - dee - hi - da,   Yoo - hi - dee,   yoo - hi - da.

p

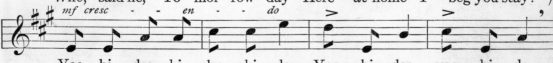

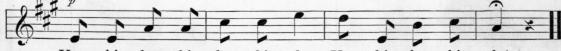

Yoo - hi - dee   hi - dee - hi - da,   Yoo - hi - dee - hi - da!

AMERICA, THE BEAUTIFUL
(MATERNA)

Katharine Lee Bates

Samuel A. Ward

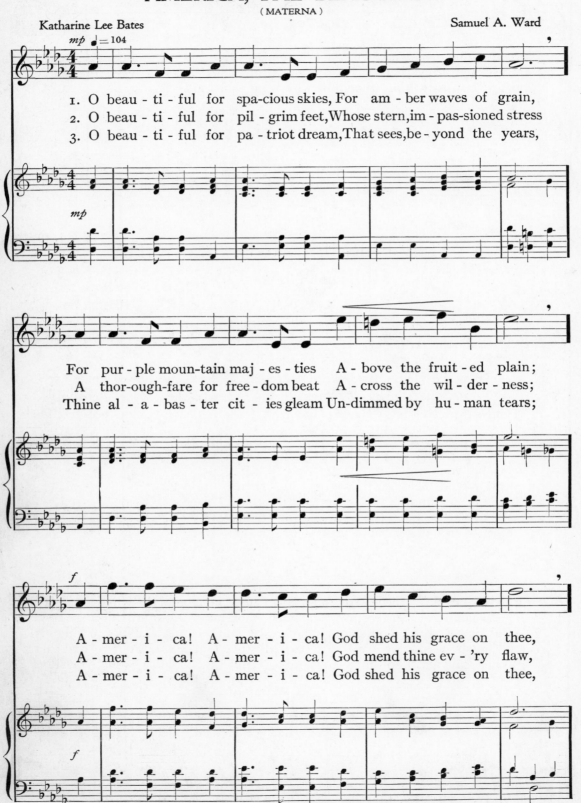

1. O beau - ti - ful for spa-cious skies, For am - ber waves of grain,
2. O beau - ti - ful for pil - grim feet, Whose stern, im - pas-sioned stress
3. O beau - ti - ful for pa - triot dream, That sees, be - yond the years,

For pur - ple moun-tain maj - es - ties A - bove the fruit - ed plain;
A thor-ough-fare for free - dom beat A - cross the wil - der - ness;
Thine al - a - bas - ter cit - ies gleam Un-dimmed by hu - man tears;

A - mer - i - ca! A - mer - i - ca! God shed his grace on thee,
A - mer - i - ca! A - mer - i - ca! God mend thine ev - 'ry flaw,
A - mer - i - ca! A - mer - i - ca! God shed his grace on thee,

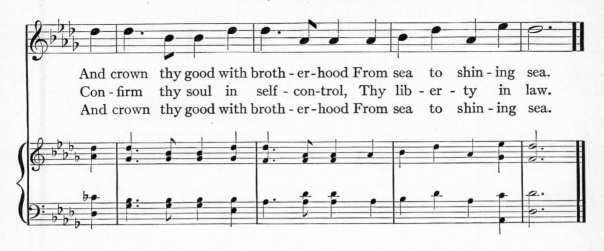

And crown thy good with broth - er-hood From sea to shin - ing sea.
Con - firm thy soul in self - con-trol, Thy lib - er - ty in law.
And crown thy good with broth - er-hood From sea to shin - ing sea.

CHRISTMAS DAY

English Melody

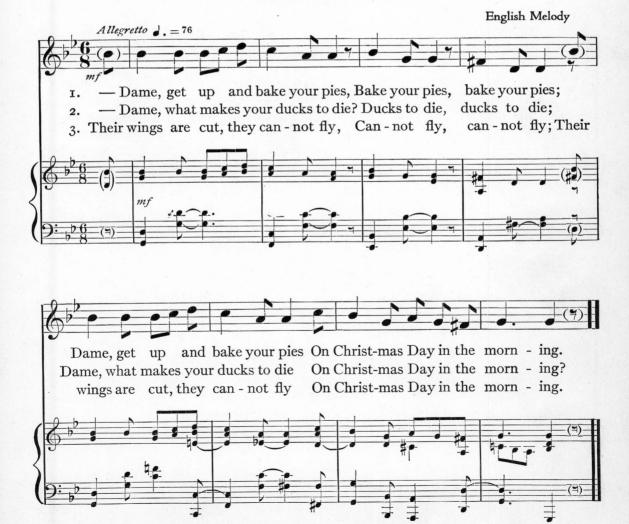

Allegretto ♪. = 76

mf

1. — Dame, get up and bake your pies, Bake your pies, bake your pies;
2. — Dame, what makes your ducks to die? Ducks to die, ducks to die;
3. Their wings are cut, they can - not fly, Can - not fly, can - not fly; Their

mf

Dame, get up and bake your pies On Christ-mas Day in the morn - ing.
Dame, what makes your ducks to die On Christ-mas Day in the morn - ing?
wings are cut, they can - not fly On Christ-mas Day in the morn - ing.

ST. VALENTINE'S DAY

N. Grier Parke

Arthur Edward Johnstone

1. To-day I gave my heart a-way And you are the one I
2. I write to you, my Love, to say Your Val-en-tine I would

chose, . . A se-cret that no one knows. Go, see! My
be; . . Oh, tell me that you'll a-gree! Ah me! My

heart! Rest-ing there by the gar-den gate, Send me your
heart! Cu-pid's ar-row has pierced it through; Now I am

an-swer, I scarce can wait; Read there what I would say, I have
send-ing it, Love, to you. Take this, keep it, I pray; Let this

molto ritard.

giv - en my heart a - way, For this   is   good St. Val -en-tine's Day.
gift with my true Love stay, For this   is   good St. Val -en-tine's Day.

molto ritard.

THE LAND OF NOD

Robert Louis Stevenson   Arthur Edward Johnstone

With a gentle, swaying motion ♩= 72

1. From break - fast   on   all   through the
2. All   by   my - self   I   have to

day,   At home a - mong my friends   I   stay;   But ev - 'ry
go,   With none to   tell   me what   to   do;   All a -

night   I   go a - broad A - far   in - to the land   of Nod.
lone be - side the streams And up   the moun-tain-sides   of dreams.

MAY

Isidore Luckstone

Blue-eyed vio-lets peep-ing up Thro' the fra-grant mold,

Blue-birds sing a song of joy Through the morn-ing's gold.

Ap-ple boughs are pink and white, Wav-ing in the breeze; Oh, what hap-py

hours for all Un-der May-time trees. . . O ho! . . . . . .

THE NIGHTINGALE

K. D.

Polish Air

1. Thro' the woods the night-in-gale Pours her sil-ver song,
2. Lark and thrush their mu-sic hush, Soft-ly fades the light;

Un-der the mag-ic moon of May Car-ol-ing all night long.
On-ly the lone-ly night-in-gale Sings her song at night.

MORNING BY THE LAKE

Ira Barton

A. Maillart
From the opera "The Dragoons of Villars"

1. In the morn-ing ver-y ear-ly, When the
2. There's a flut-t'ring and a rus-tling, There's a
3. Such a sound of joy-ful sing-ing Sets the

grass with dew is pearl-y, There's a stir-ring in the
twit-t'ring and a bus-tling And at last a burst of
pop-lar leaves a-swing-ing, And the hill and dale are

pop-lars As the birds be-gin to wake.
mu-sic In the pop-lars by the lake.
ring-ing With the mu-sic by the lake.

HARVEST SONG

Melissa Murphy

Clarence Butler

Joyfully ♩. = 76

1. Heigh - ho! Let's be go - ing Down the mead - ow, bright in the sun!
2. Heigh - ho! Youth and maid - en, Heap the sheaves that shine in the sun!
3. Heigh - ho! Start the fid - dle! Lads and lass - es, in at the door!

Now's the time for bar - ley mow-ing; Heigh - ho! Sum-mer is done!
See the heav - y wag - ons lad - en; Heigh - ho! Reap-ing is done!
Up the side and down the mid - dle; Come now! Out on the floor!

Val - ley and plain rip - en a - gain, Bear-ing a wealth of gold - en grain.
Gay - ly we come, gay - ly we come, Bear-ing the gold - en har-vest home.
Can-dles are bright, eyes are a - light, Danc-ing the Har - vest Home to-night.

LITTLE LAME GIRL

Translated by K. D.

French Folk Song

Allegretto moderato ♩ = 96

1. Lit-tle lame girl, where are you go-ing?
2. To the for-est I am go-ing.
3. Why to the for-est are you go-ing?
4. I shall pick the vio-lets grow-ing.

Too-ro-lay, Too-ro-

lay.

Lit-tle lame girl, where are you go-ing?
To the for-est I am go-ing.
Why to the for-est are you go-ing?
I shall pick the vio-lets growing.

Too-ro-lay, lay, lay.

5. What'll you do with violets growing? etc. (twice)
6. They're to give to my little sisters. etc. (twice)
7. Where, O where are your little sisters? etc. (twice)
8. Here is one of my little sisters. etc. (twice)
9. Are there more of your little sisters? etc. (twice)
10. Here's another of my little sisters. etc. (twice)

DIRECTIONS: The players stand in line while one girl walks up and down in front of them, limping and singing the stanzas alternately with them. At the eighth stanza the lame girl chooses a little sister from the group and leads her out. The ninth and tenth stanzas are repeated as many times as there are players, after which the game ends.

DANCING WITH ROSA

Flemish Folk Dance

Allegretto con grazia ♩. = 72

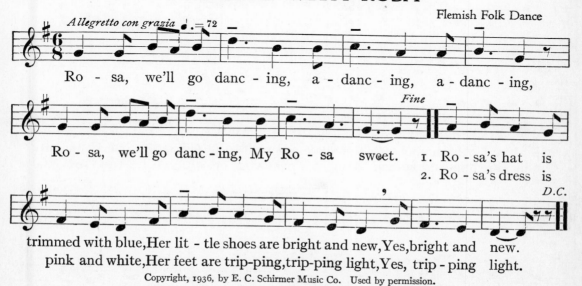

Ro-sa, we'll go danc-ing, a-danc-ing, a-danc-ing,
Ro-sa, we'll go danc-ing, My Ro-sa sweet.
1. Ro-sa's hat is
2. Ro-sa's dress is

trimmed with blue, Her lit-tle shoes are bright and new, Yes, bright and new.
pink and white, Her feet are trip-ping, trip-ping light, Yes, trip-ping light.

Copyright, 1936, by E. C. Schirmer Music Co. Used by permission.

LULLABY

K. D.

Katherine Davis

Andante ♩ = 88

1. Lull - a - by - by, my dar - ling, With
2. Lull - a - by - by, my dar - ling, As

With pedal

soft pet - aled hands, Ros - y white! . . . . Like a bloom in the
fra - grant and sweet As the May! . . . . Like a bird in the

pear tree the high moon is hung, Gold - en bright! . . . Like a
pear tree the gold moon will shine Till the day! . . . But

bird thro' the branch - es the pale moon doth fly, Like a bird on my
when in the morn - ing you o - pen your eyes She'll be fad - ed and

bo - som my ba - by doth lie. And I'll sing her to
lost in the light of the skies, Rock'd to sleep with the

sleep with a soft lull - a - by, All the night . . . .
sound of . the wind's lull - a - by, Far a - way . . . .

. . . . Lull - a - by - by, Lull - a -
. . . . Lull - a - by - by, Lull - a -

by - by, All the night. . . . . .
by - by, Far a - way. . . . . .

SPRING'S MESSENGER

English version by Maxwell Gaddis

Robert Schumann

Allegretto ♩ = 69

1. "Cuck-oo, cuck-oo," sounds far and near, Let us be sing-ing,
2. Cuck-oo, cuck-oo, on with your song! Come to the wood-land,
3. Cuck-oo, cuck-oo! Ah, you are gay! Sing, jol-ly fel-low,

let us be spring-ing, Let us be sing-ing and spring-ing!
come to the mead-ow, Come to the wood-land and mead-ow!
mu-sic so mel-low, Sing us your mu-sic so mel-low.

A-pril soon will be here! A-pril soon will be here!
Spring-time fol-lows a-long! Springtime fol-lows a-long!
Win-ter has-tens a-way! Win-ter has-tens a-way!

WHEN THINGS GROW UP

N. Grier Parke

Arthur Edward Johnstone

THE LADYBIRD

German Song
Arranged by Johannes Brahms

1. O La - dy - bird, so small, so fair, Come on my
2. O pret - ty La - dy - bird, fly now Un - to my
3. O La - dy - bird, haste, fly a - way! See, thy house

hand, come on my hand And I will nev - er hurt thee,
friend, un - to my friend, And he will nev - er hurt thee,
burns, thy chil - dren call; Dost not thou hear them cry - ing?

And I will nev - er fright - en thee; Thy pret - ty wings I want to
And he will nev - er fright - en thee; Thy pret - ty wings he wants to
Oh, sore - ly, sad - ly do they weep, The wick - ed spi - der round thee

see,   Thy bright wings,   thy bright wings please me ev - er!
see,   We greet thee,   we both will greet thee ev - er!
spins,   So fly then,   a - way then now   go fly - ing!

THE GUARDIAN ANGEL

German Folk Song
Arranged by Johannes Brahms for
Robert and Clara Schumann's children

English text adapted by K. D.

Slowly ♩ = 96

1. Dear Guardian An - gel, sweet and kind, Oh, will you walk be - side me?
2. Now when the sun   de-scends the sky, Down in - to dark - ness go - ing,
3. Pa-tient you stand be - side my bed While thro' the night I'm sleeping;

How can I   fear when you are near, Read-y to watch and guide me!
I need no   light to shine on high, O'er me your wings are - glowing!
Safe-ly I   rest and feel no dread; My soul is in . your keeping.

HUNTING THE HARE

Welsh

Vivace ♩. = 72

1. O - ver hill and plain they're bounding, Thro' the air they seem to fly;
2. When the day's glad sport is o - ver, Seat - ed in the bar-on's hall

Hark! the mer - ry horn is sounding, List! the hunt-er's jov - i - al cry!
Round the fes - tive board dis - cov - er Gal - lant hunt-ers one and all!

Now thro' din - gle, dell, and hol - low, Dart they on at fear - less pace;
Laugh-ing loud - ly, jok - ing, sing-ing, As the wine goes round a - pace,

Oh, what joy the hounds to fol - low, There's no pleas-ure like the chase!
While the an - cient roof is ring-ing With the glo - ries of the chase.

GARDEN IN THE SNOW

Anthony Gillespie

Jacques Offenbach

Andantino ♩ = 80

1. Sum - mer is fled, Ros - es are dead; With-ered ev - 'ry
2. Yet do not sigh, Time pass - es by; Buds are on - ly

flow - er In my gar-den bow - er. Sky's gray and low,
sleep - ing, Safe in win-ter's keep - ing. Warm suns will glow,

Winds soft-ly blow; Bur - ied is my gar - den, Un - der-neath the snow.
Warm breezes blow, I shall find my gar - den Un - der-neath the snow.

SINGIN' JOHNNY

Anon.

Old Sailor Chantey

Allegro moderato ♩. = 69

1. They call me sing - in' John - ny; . Yo ho, . yo
2. They call me smil - in' John - ny; . Yo ho, . yo

ho, . Be-cause my tunes are bon - ny, . Yo ho, ho, ho! .
ho, . Be-cause my face is bon - ny, . Yo ho, ho, ho! .

IN MY BIRCH CANOE

1. In my birch ca - noe, In my birch ca - noe, Down the
2. When the ea - gle flies, When the ea - gle flies Thro' the
3. When the run - ning deer, When the run - ning deer, Thro' the

riv - er wide, Down the riv - er blue, In my
morn - ing light, Thro' the morn - ing skies, When the
for - est green Seeks the wa - ter clear, When the

birch ca - noe, In my birch ca - noe, Down the
ea - gle flies Thro' the morn - ing skies, Down the
run - ning deer Seeks the wa - ter clear, Down the

long, long riv - er I'll go, Down the long, long riv - er I'll go.
long, long riv - er I'll go, Down the long, long riv - er I'll go.
long, long riv - er I'll go, Down the long, long riv - er I'll go.

*Each stanza may be accompanied by soft drum beating on a real drum or with pencils on desks.

ADITIONAL SONGS*

O A-HUNTING WE WILL GO

Old English   ♩ = 92   English Folk Song

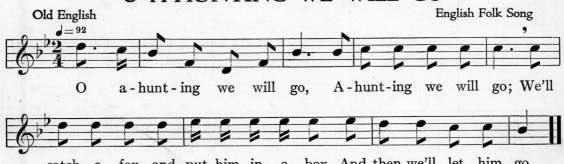

O a-hunt-ing we will go, A-hunt-ing we will go; We'll

catch a fox and put him in a box, And then we'll let him go.

GOOD MORNING

J. Lilian Vandevere   John E. West
Moderato ♩ = 69

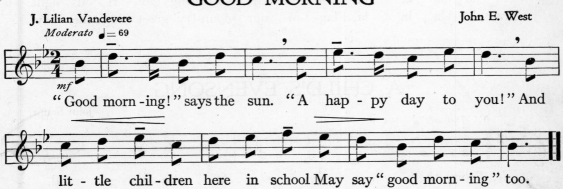

"Good morn-ing!" says the sun. "A hap-py day to you!" And

lit-tle chil-dren here in school May say "good morn-ing" too.

MILKWEED

J. Lilian Vandevere   John E. West
Allegretto ♩. = 58   *cresc.*

The milk-weed keeps her seeds at home Till some fine au-tumn day, When

each one spreads a par-a-chute And gen-tly sails a-way.

* These songs will be found useful for beginners; many of them are ideal material for sight reading, words and music.

REVEILLE

Dutch Folk Song

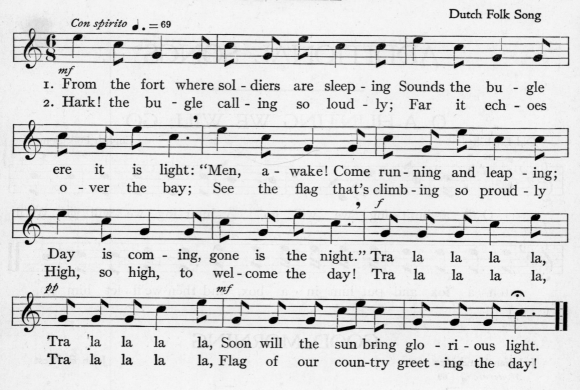

Con spirito ♩. = 69

mf

1. From the fort where sol - diers are sleep - ing Sounds the bu - gle
2. Hark! the bu - gle call - ing so loud - ly; Far it ech - oes

ere it is light: "Men, a - wake! Come run - ning and leap - ing;
o - ver the bay; See the flag that's climb - ing so proud - ly

Day is com - ing, gone is the night." Tra la la la la,
High, so high, to wel - come the day! Tra la la la la,

pp   *mf*

Tra la la la la, Soon will the sun bring glo - ri - ous light.
Tra la la la la, Flag of our coun - try greet - ing the day!

A CHILD'S EVENSONG

John Stainer

Andante ♩ = 104

1. From the heav'n a - bove us, 'Mid the an - gels mild,
2. Boun - teous - ly he gives us Food and rai - ment still,

Looks a lov - ing Fa - ther Down on ev - 'ry child.
Gra - cious - ly he keeps us From each threat - 'ning ill.

Ten - der - ly he lis - tens When he hears us pray,
Praise the lov - ing Fa - ther, Of his good - ness tell;

Faith - ful - ly he guides us On our earth - ly way.
He will not for - sake us, He doth love us well.

A CHILD'S PRAYER

Ignaz J. Pleyel

Moderato ♩ = 80

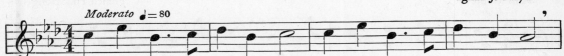

1. King of Heav'n, by all a - dored, Thee we name our Fa - ther, Lord;
2. Great and small in thee re - joice, Birds and flow'rs o - bey thy voice;

Sun and stars are in thy hands, O - ceans wide and pleas-ant lands.
Thou, whose love is ev - 'ry - where, Hear, this day, thy chil-dren's prayer!

PRAISE THE LORD

Wolfgang Amadeus Mozart

Moderato ♩ = 60

1. Praise the Lord in the heav - ens! Praise ye him in the
2. Fire and hail, snow and va - por, All ful - fill - ing his

height! Praise ye him, all his an - gels! Praise him, all ye stars of light!
word, Come, both young men and maid-ens, Praise the name of the Lord!

THANKSGIVING

Anna L. Barbauld

Johann R. Ahle

With dignity ♩ = 88

mf

1. Praise to God, im - mor-tal praise, For the love that crowns our days;
2. Flocks that whit - en all the plain, Yel - low sheaves of rip - en'd grain,
3. All that Spring, with bounteous hand, Scat-ters o'er the smil - ing land;
4. These to thee, my God, we owe, Source whence all our bless-ings flow;

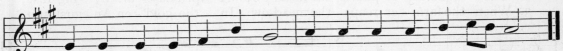

Bounteous source of ev - 'ry joy, Let thy praise our tongues em-ploy!
Clouds that drop their fat-'ning dews, Suns that temp'rate warmth dif-fuse.
All that lib - 'ral Au-tumn pours From her rich o'er-flow - ing stores.
And for these my soul shall raise Grate-ful vows and sol - emn praise.

THE UNFORTUNATE CHICKENS

Ann White

French Folk Song

Allegretto ♩ = 96

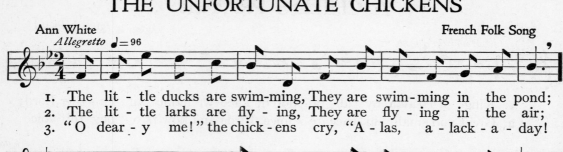

1. The lit - tle ducks are swim-ming, They are swim-ming in the pond;
2. The lit - tle larks are fly - ing, They are fly - ing in the air;
3. "O dear - y me!" the chick - ens cry, "A - las, a - lack - a - day!

The lit - tle chick - ens stand and gaze Up - on the bank be - yond.
The lit - tle chick - ens on the ground Can on - ly stand and stare.
We can - not swim, we can - not fly, So here we have to stay!"

MARY JANE

Ann White

English Folk Tune

Moderato ♩ = 84

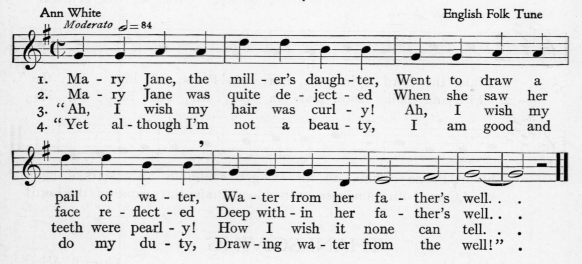

1. Ma - ry Jane, the mill - er's daugh - ter, Went to draw a
2. Ma - ry Jane was quite de - ject - ed When she saw her
3. "Ah, I wish my hair was curl - y! Ah, I wish my
4. "Yet al - though I'm not a beau - ty, I am good and

pail of wa - ter, Wa - ter from her fa - ther's well. . .
face re - flect - ed Deep with - in her fa - ther's well. . .
teeth were pearl - y! How I wish it none can tell. . .
do my du - ty, Draw - ing wa - ter from the well!" .

THE MEADOW

Ann White

Lowell Mason

Andantino ♩ = 108

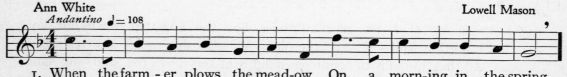

1. When the farm - er plows the mead-ow On a morn-ing in the spring,
2. When the farm - er plants the mead-ow, A - pril days are fly - ing fast;
3. When the farm - er reaps the mead-ow In the gold - en Au - gust sun,

In the branches, scarce-ly bud-ded, You can hear the rob - in sing.
Larks and thrush-es in the bush-es Know that spring has come at last.
Hear the lo - cust sad - ly shrill-ing: "Sum-mer days are al-most done."

MAKE BELIEVE

Ann White
Allegretto ♩ = 96

Czechoslovakian Folk Tune

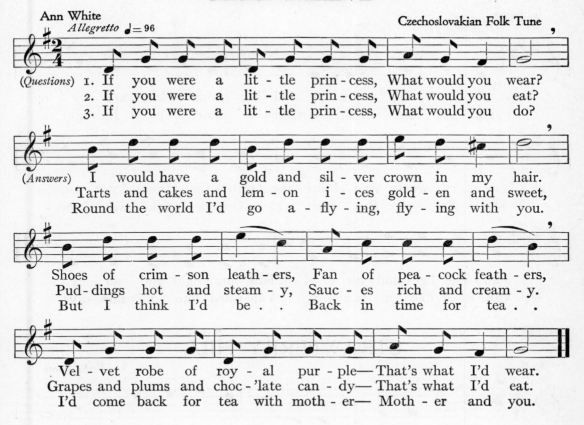

(Questions) 1. If you were a lit - tle prin - cess, What would you wear?
2. If you were a lit - tle prin - cess, What would you eat?
3. If you were a lit - tle prin - cess, What would you do?

(Answers) I would have a gold and sil - ver crown in my hair.
Tarts and cakes and lem - on i - ces gold - en and sweet,
Round the world I'd go a - fly - ing, fly - ing with you.

Shoes of crim - son leath - ers, Fan of pea - cock feath - ers,
Pud - dings hot and steam - y, Sauc - es rich and cream - y,
But I think I'd be . . Back in time for tea . .

Vel - vet robe of roy - al pur - ple—That's what I'd wear.
Grapes and plums and choc - 'late can - dy—That's what I'd eat.
I'd come back for tea with moth - er— Moth - er and you.

A CAROL FOR CHRISTMAS

J. L. V.
Simply ♩ = 132

J. Lilian Vandevere

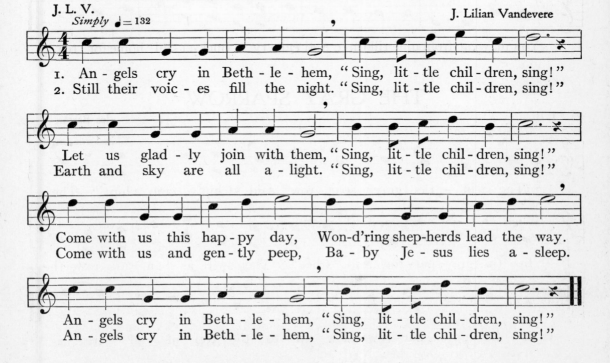

1. An - gels cry in Beth - le - hem, "Sing, lit - tle chil - dren, sing!"
2. Still their voic - es fill the night. "Sing, lit - tle chil - dren, sing!"

Let us glad - ly join with them, "Sing, lit - tle chil - dren, sing!"
Earth and sky are all a - light. "Sing, lit - tle chil - dren, sing!"

Come with us this hap - py day, Won - d'ring shep - herds lead the way.
Come with us and gen - tly peep, Ba - by Je - sus lies a - sleep.

An - gels cry in Beth - le - hem, "Sing, lit - tle chil - dren, sing!"
An - gels cry in Beth - le - hem, "Sing, lit - tle chil - dren, sing!"

A SNOWFLAKE

Ira Barton

Carl Reinecke

1. Oh - oh - oh!   See the fall-ing snow! Flakes are fly - ing
2. Oh - oh - oh! Fair - y flakes of snow! Once I caught a

ev - 'ry - where And whirl-ing thro' the frost - y   air,
star - ry one, But when   I looked, the flake was gone,

Fall - ing light and air - y, Fall - ing light and air - y.
Van-ished like a fair - y, Van-ished like a fair - y.

STRAWBERRY HILL

L. F.

Lydia Foote

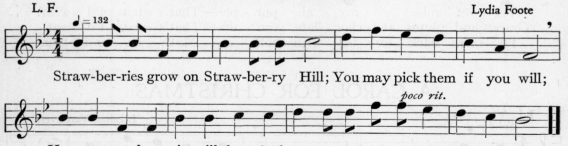

Straw-ber-ries grow on Straw-ber-ry Hill; You may pick them if you will;

You may eat from nine till three And car - ry a buck-et-ful home for tea.

THE GRAY SPARROW

I. B.

Ira Barton

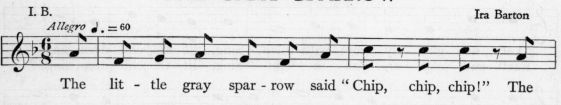

The   lit - tle gray spar - row said "Chip,   chip, chip!" The

lit - tle gray spar - row said "Chee!" Then swift as an   ar - row, the

lit - tle gray spar - row Flew up to the top of the   tree! .

THE BELLMAN

L. F.

Lydia Foote

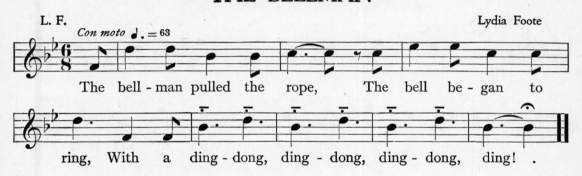

The bell-man pulled the rope, The bell be-gan to ring, With a ding-dong, ding-dong, ding-dong, ding! .

THE CALL TO PLAY

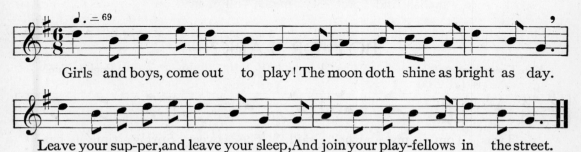

Girls and boys, come out to play! The moon doth shine as bright as day. Leave your sup-per, and leave your sleep, And join your play-fellows in the street.

BRIGHT STAR

L. F.

Lydia Foote

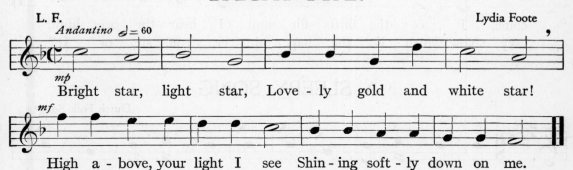

Bright star, light star, Love-ly gold and white star! High a-bove, your light I see Shin-ing soft-ly down on me.

DOWN IN THE WELL

M. G.

Maxwell Gaddis

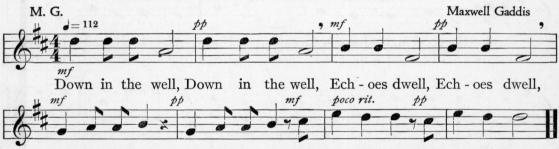

Down in the well, Down in the well, Ech-oes dwell, Ech-oes dwell, Clear as can be, Clear as can be They an-swer me—They an-swer me.

140

MY LADY'S GARDEN

How does my la - dy's gar - den grow?

How does my la - dy's gar - den grow? With sil - ver bells and

cock - le shells, And pret - ty maids all in a row! .

BOY OR LARK?

Kate Greenaway

English Tune

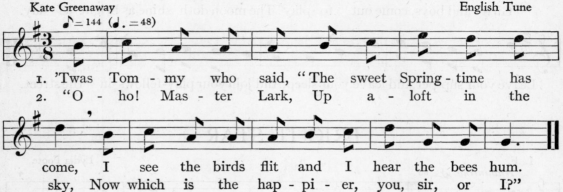

1. 'Twas Tom - my who said, "The sweet Spring - time has
2. "O - ho! Mas - ter Lark, Up a - loft in the

come, I see the birds flit and I hear the bees hum.
sky, Now which is the hap - pi - er, you, sir, or I?"

A SLEEPY SONG

Dutch Folk Song

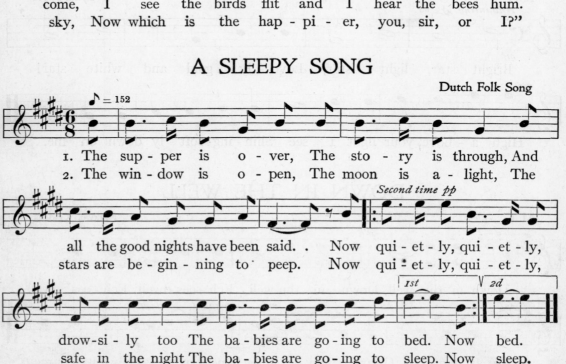

1. The sup - per is o - ver, The sto - ry is through, And
2. The win - dow is o - pen, The moon is a - light, The

Second time pp

all the good nights have been said. . Now qui - et - ly, qui - et - ly,
stars are be - gin - ning to peep. Now qui - et - ly, qui - et - ly,

1st   2d

drow - si - ly too The ba - bies are go - ing to bed. Now bed.
safe in the night The ba - bies are go - ing to sleep. Now sleep.

APRIL

F. A. Gevaert

1. No cloud in the shin - ing sky, No sign of a storm we spy.
2. The daf - fo - dils gen - tly sway, The tu - lips are brave and gay;

Where ferns un-curl, Where the leaves un-furl, See A - pril hur-ry- ing by.
They all ad-vance In a spring-time dance, With A-pril show-ing the way.

BONFIRES

German Folk Song

1. When Au - tumn days are la - zy, And lone - ly crows be -
2. And while the fires are burn - ing, In drift - ing curls the

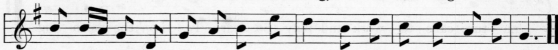

gin to call, The frost - y air is ha - zy, With bon-fires in the Fall.
smoke will fly, As though the leaves were turn-ing, To wave a last good-by.

THE NUT TREE

Old Song

1. I had a lit - tle nut tree, Noth - ing would it bear .
2. Her dress was all of crim - son, Coal black was her hair; She

But a sil - ver nut - meg And a gold - en pear. The
ask'd me for my nut tree And my gold - en pear. I

King of Spain's daugh - ter Came to vis - it me, And
said, "So fair a prin - cess Nev - er did I see, I'll

all . . for the sake Of my lit - tle nut tree.
give to you the fruit Of my lit - tle nut tree."

MORNING SONG

Anonymous

English, 18th Century

Con moto ♩. = 88

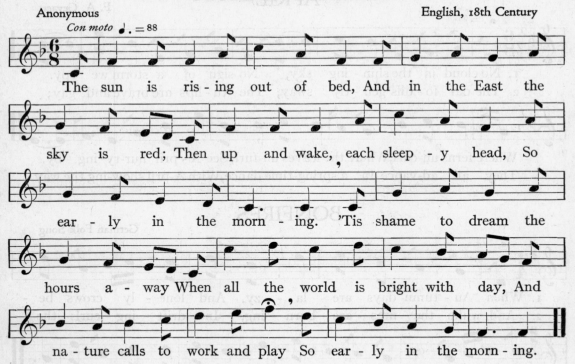

The sun is ris-ing out of bed, And in the East the
sky is red; Then up and wake, each sleep-y head, So
ear-ly in the morn-ing. 'Tis shame to dream the
hours a-way When all the world is bright with day, And
na-ture calls to work and play So ear-ly in the morn-ing.

TO LONDON TOWN

English

♩ = 132

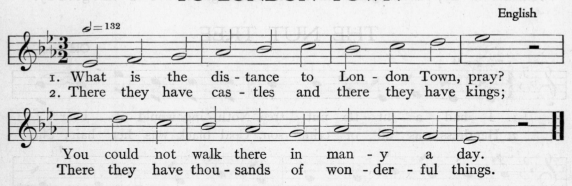

1. What is the dis-tance to Lon-don Town, pray?
2. There they have cas-tles and there they have kings;

You could not walk there in man-y a day.
There they have thou-sands of won-der-ful things.

PETS

J. L. V.

J. Lilian Vandevere

♩ = 84

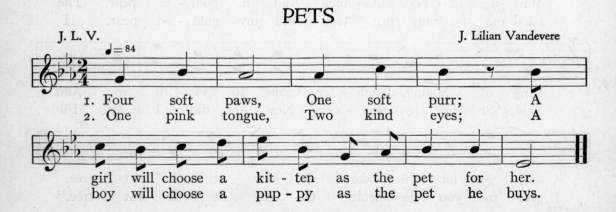

1. Four soft paws, One soft purr; A
2. One pink tongue, Two kind eyes; A

girl will choose a kit-ten as the pet for her.
boy will choose a pup-py as the pet he buys.

FOLLOW ME, FULL OF GLEE

Gaily ♩ = 84

mf

1. Chil-dren go, to and fro, In a mer-ry, pret-ty row;
2. Birds are free, so are we, And we live as hap-pi-ly;
3. Work is done, play's be-gun, Now we have our laugh and fun;

Foot-steps light, fac-es bright, 'Tis a hap-py, hap-py sight;
Work we do, stud-y too, Learn-ing dai-ly some-thing new;
Hap-py days, pret-ty plays, And no naugh-ty, naugh-ty ways.

mp *cresc. . . . .*

Swift-ly turn-ing round and round, Do not look up-on the ground;
Then we laugh, and dance, and sing, Gay as birds or an-y-thing.
Hold-ing fast each oth-er's hand, We're a hap-py, cheer-ful band;

mf *mp*

Fol-low me, full of glee, Sing-ing mer-ri-ly.
Fol-low me, full of glee, Sing-ing mer-ri-ly. } Sing-ing mer-ri-ly,
Fol-low me, full of glee, Sing-ing mer-ri-ly.

cresc. . . . .

mer-ri-ly, mer-ri-ly, Sing-ing mer-ri-ly, mer-ri-ly, mer-ri-ly,

mf

Fol-low me, full of glee, Sing-ing mer-ri-ly.

ON THE WINTER WIND

Christina Rossetti   Czech Folk Song

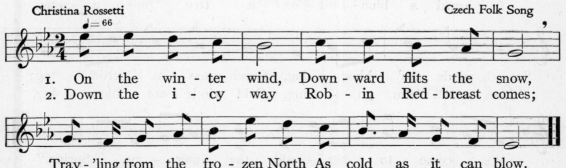

♩ = 66

1. On the win-ter wind, Down-ward flits the snow,
2. Down the i-cy way Rob-in Red-breast comes;

Trav-'ling from the fro-zen North As cold as it can blow.
Let him in to feel your fire And toss him of your crumbs.

TWINKLE, LITTLE STAR

Jane Taylor

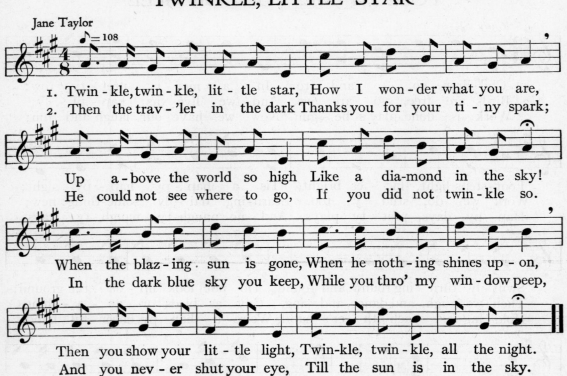

1. Twin - kle, twin - kle, lit - tle star, How I won - der what you are,
2. Then the trav - 'ler in the dark Thanks you for your ti - ny spark;

Up a - bove the world so high Like a dia-mond in the sky!
He could not see where to go, If you did not twin - kle so.

When the blaz - ing sun is gone, When he noth - ing shines up - on,
In the dark blue sky you keep, While you thro' my win - dow peep,

Then you show your lit - tle light, Twin-kle, twin - kle, all the night.
And you nev - er shut your eye, Till the sun is in the sky.

EARLY ONE MORNING

Anonymous

English Folk Song

Moderato ♩ = 80

1. Ear - ly one morn - ing, be - fore the sun had ris - en,
2. One Au - tumn af - ter - noon, just as the sun was set - ting,

I heard a blue - bird in the fields gay - ly sing,
I heard a blue - bird on a tree pipe a song,

"South winds are blow - ing, Green grass is grow - ing;
"Fare - well! We're go - ing, Cold winds are blow - ing,

We come to her - ald the mer - ry Spring."
But we'll be back when the days grow long."

THE LITTLE SHIP

English Folk Song

With swinging rhythm ♩. = 66

1. I saw a ship a - sail - ing, A - sail - ing on the sea! And
2. The four - and - twen-ty sail - ors That stood be-tween the decks Were

oh, it was all lad - en With pret - ty things for thee! There were
four-and-twen - ty white mice With chains a - bout their necks; The .

com- fits in the cab - in, And ap - ples in the hold, And the
cap - tain was a lit - tle duck With a pack - et on his back, And

spread-ing sails were made of silk, And the masts were made of gold.
when the ship be - gan to move, The cap-tain cried, "Quack! Quack!"

SING A SONG OF SIXPENCE

Mother Goose

J. W. Elliott

Allegretto ♩ = 58

1. — Sing a song of six - pence, A pock - et full of rye; —
2. The king was in the count-ing - house Count-ing out his mon- ey; The

Four - and - twen - ty black -birds Baked in a pie; —
queen was in the par - lor, Eat - ing bread and hon - ey; The

When the pie was o - pened, The birds be - gan to sing, —
maid was in the gar - den, Hang - ing out the clothes; There

Was - n't that a dain - ty dish To set be - fore a king?
came a lit - tle dick - y bird And popped up - on her nose!

SLEEPYHEAD

Ira Barton

French Folk Song

With swinging rhythm ♩. = 76

Oh, you sleep-y-head, Oh, you sleep-y-head, Oh, you sleep-y-head
Ma - ry! Leave your pil - low, Oh, leave your pil - low And come a - way with
me! Through the A - pril weath - er Let us go to - geth - er
O - ver mead-ow and o - ver mountain To find the shin - ing sea. .

HERE AND THERE

J. L. V.

J. Lilian Vandevere

♩ = 76

1. I've pat - ent leath - er slip - pers, Or san - dals, if I
2. My train can run on switch - es, The en - gine has a

choose, But a child in Ja - pan Goes in click - ing wood - en shoes.
light, But a child in Ja - pan Flies a pret - ty pa - per kite.

GEORGIE PORGIE

Mother Goose

English Folk Song

Gaily ♩. = 72

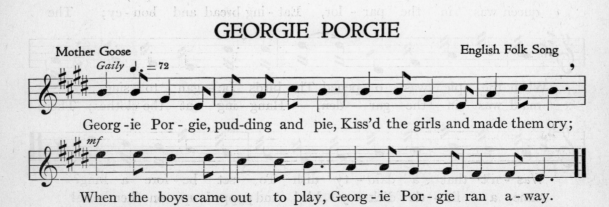

Georg - ie Por - gie, pud-ding and pie, Kiss'd the girls and made them cry;

When the boys came out to play, Georg - ie Por - gie ran a - way.

POLLY THE PONY

CHRISTMAS BELLS

SLEEP-TIME

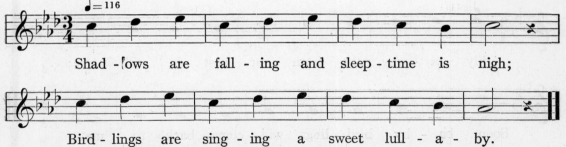

CHRISTOPHER COLUMBUS

J. L. V.

J. Lilian Vandevere

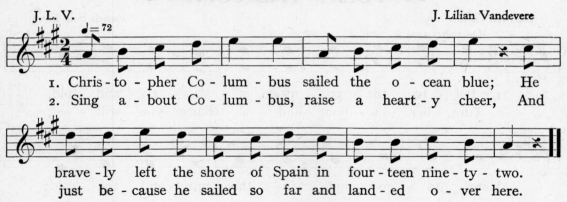

1. Chris-to-pher Co-lum-bus sailed the o-cean blue; He
2. Sing a-bout Co-lum-bus, raise a heart-y cheer, And

brave-ly left the shore of Spain in four-teen nine-ty-two.
just be-cause he sailed so far and land-ed o-ver here.

CHRISTMAS TIME

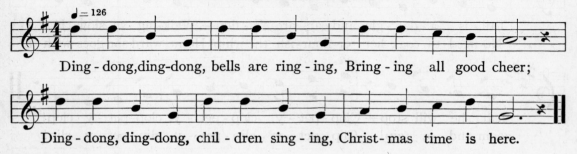

Ding-dong, ding-dong, bells are ring-ing, Bring-ing all good cheer;

Ding-dong, ding-dong, chil-dren sing-ing, Christ-mas time is here.

A SONG OF PRAISE

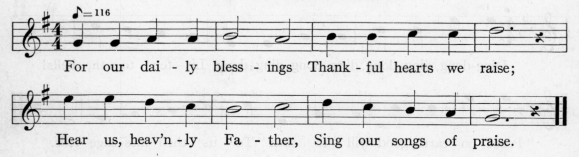

For our dai-ly bless-ings Thank-ful hearts we raise;

Hear us, heav'n-ly Fa-ther, Sing our songs of praise.

BABY BIRDLINGS

Fly a-way, fly from our nest in the tree;

Soon ba-by bird-lings will come back to me.

OUR SONG

Sweet - ly, soft - ly, all the day long,

Light - ly, bright - ly, sing we our song.

THE BUTTERFLY

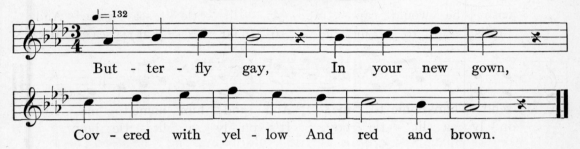

But - ter - fly gay, In your new gown,

Cov - ered with yel - low And red and brown.

JACK FROST

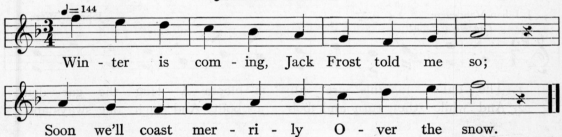

Win - ter is com - ing, Jack Frost told me so;

Soon we'll coast mer - ri - ly O - ver the snow.

WORK AND PLAY

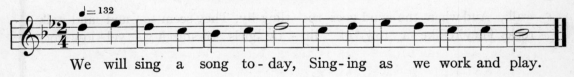

We will sing a song to - day, Sing - ing as we work and play.

TICK–TOCK

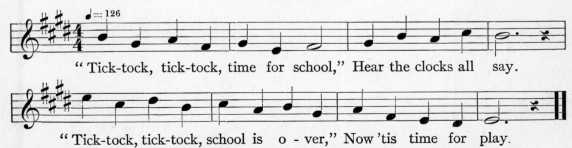

" Tick-tock, tick-tock, time for school," Hear the clocks all say.

" Tick-tock, tick-tock, school is o - ver," Now 'tis time for play.

A SONG FROM THE SHORE

James Whitcomb Riley

Ira Foote

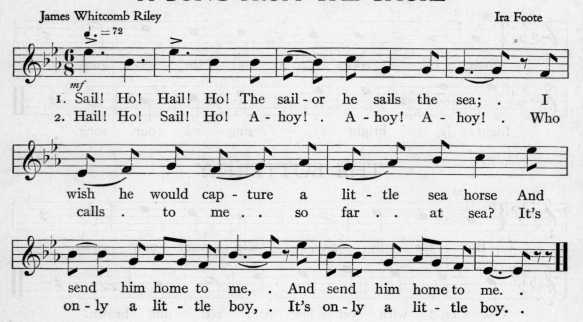

1. Sail! Ho! Hail! Ho! The sail-or he sails the sea; . I
2. Hail! Ho! Sail! Ho! A-hoy! . A-hoy! A-hoy! . Who

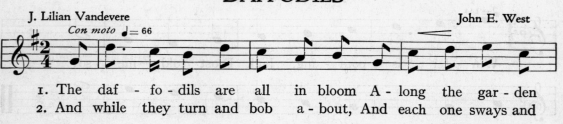

wish he would cap-ture a lit-tle sea horse And
calls . to me . . so far . . at sea? It's

send him home to me, . And send him home to me. .
on-ly a lit-tle boy, . It's on-ly a lit-tle boy. .

DAFFODILS

J. Lilian Vandevere

John E. West

Con moto ♩ = 66

1. The daf-fo-dils are all in bloom A-long the gar-den
2. And while they turn and bob a-bout, And each one sways and

walk, And when the wind goes rus-tling by, They seem to nod and talk.
rocks, They're like a row of lit-tle girls In starch-y yel-low frocks.

CLASSIFIED INDEX

ALPHABETICAL INDEX